Teacher's Resource Masters

GRADE 4 VOLUME 1

Topics 1–7

Home-School Connection Letters
Pick a Project
enVision® STEM Activities
Daily Review
Reteach to Build Understanding
Build Mathematical Literacy
Enrichment
Fluency Practice/Assessment

enVision® Mathematics

Savvas Learning Company LLC, 15 East Midland Avenue, Paramus, NJ 07652

ISBN-13: 978-0-13-495418-9
ISBN-10: 0-13-495418-1
7 21

Grade 4
Volume 1: Topics 1–7

Topic 5
Use Strategies and Properties to Divide by 1-Digit Numbers

Topic 6
Use Operations with Whole Numbers to Solve Problems

Topic 7
Factors and Multiples

Name ___________________________

Home-School Connection
Topic **1**

Generalize Place Value Understanding

Dear Family,

Your child is learning how greater numbers are written, how place values are related, and how to compare numbers. In this topic he or she will learn about the structure of the place-value system with numbers through 1 million. This topic will also allow your child to recognize that the value of a digit depends on its place in a number and that a digit in one place represents ten times what it represents in the place to its right. This is an important skill that will allow your child to communicate mathematical ideas and reasoning.

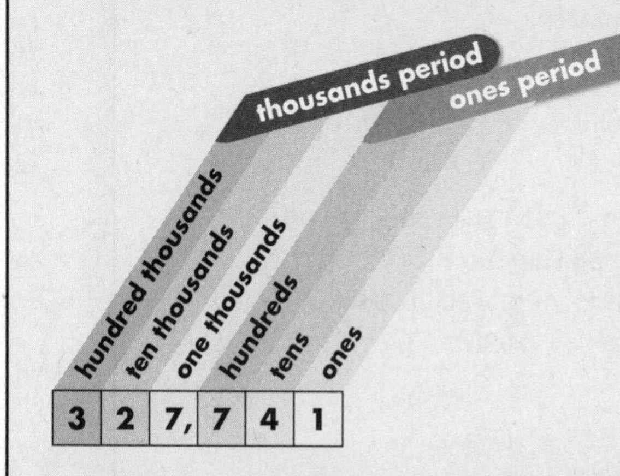

The first 7 is in the thousands place.
Its value is 7,000.
The second 7 is in the hundreds place.
Its value is 700.

Know Your Numbers

Materials index cards, paper and pencil

Make a set of number cards by writing one digit 0 through 9 on each index card. Have your child select cards and arrange them to make the greatest possible 6-digit number. Record the number. For example, if the digits are 1, 3, 5, 6, 7, and 9, the greatest number is 976,531. Then have your child rearrange the cards to make the least possible 6-digit number (135,679). Record the number. Have your child read both recorded numbers aloud. Repeat the activity several times using different 6-digit numbers.

Observe Your Child

Help your child become proficient with Mathematical Practice 4. Ask your child to write a comparison statement for two numbers using the > or < symbols. Ask your child to explain how he or she determined the answer. He or she may use a place-value chart to help explain.

Nombre ______________________________

De la escuela al hogar (en español)
Tema **1**

Hacer generalizaciones sobre el valor de posición

Estimada familia:

Su niño(a) está aprendiendo cómo se escriben los números más grandes, cómo se relacionan los valores de posición y cómo comparar números. En este tema, él o ella va a aprender sobre la estructura del sistema de valor de posición con números hasta 1 millón. También, este tema va a permitir que su niño(a) reconozca que el valor de un dígito depende de su posición en un número y que un dígito en una posición representa diez veces lo que representa en la posición a su derecha. Esta es una destreza importante que va a permitir que su niño(a) comunique ideas y razonamientos matemáticos.

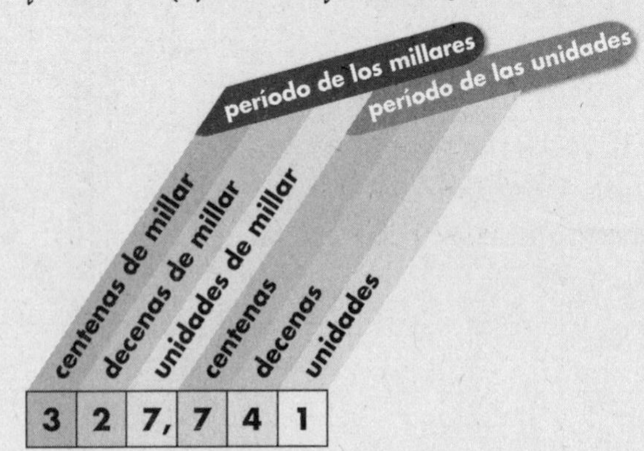

El primer 7 está en la posición de los millares; su valor es 7,000.
El segundo 7 está en la posición de las centenas; su valor es 700.

Conocer tus números

Materiales tarjetas de fichero, papel y lápiz

Haga un conjunto de tarjetas de fichero escribiendo un dígito del 0 al 9 en cada tarjeta de fichero. Pída a su niño(a) que escoja tarjetas y las ordene para formar el mayor número de 6 dígitos posible. Anote el número. Por ejemplo, si los dígitos son 1, 3, 5, 6, 7 y 9, el mayor número es 976,531. Luego, pida a su niño(a) que reordene las tarjetas para formar el menor número de 6 dígitos posible (135,679). Anote el número. Pída a su niño(a) que lea en voz alta los dos números anotados. Repita la actividad varias veces usando diferentes números de 6 dígitos.

Observe a su niño(a)

Ayude a su niño(a) a adquirir competencia en la Práctica matemática 4. Pídale que escriba un enunciado de comparación para dos números usando los símbolos $>$ o $<$. Pídale que explique cómo determinó la respuesta. Él o ella podría usar una tabla de valor de posición para ayudarse a explicar.

Name ___________________________

Pick a Project

Project 1A

How Many Bones?

Babies are born with about 300 bones. As a child ages, some of the bones fuse (join) together. An adult has 206 bones.

face: 14 bones

hand: 27 bones

foot: 26 bones

Adult human: 206 bones

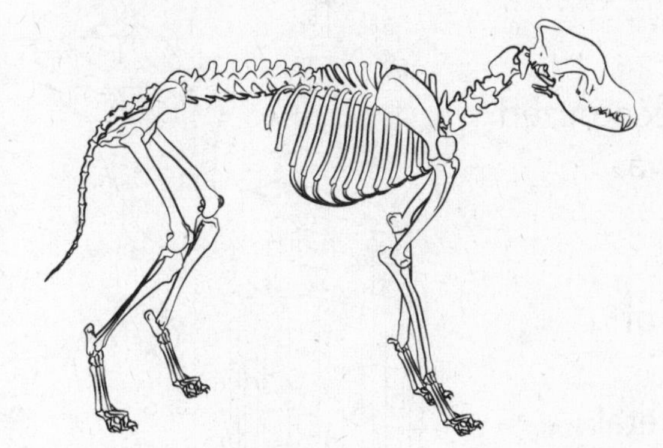

Dogs have about 320 bones. Dogs with longer tails have more bones.

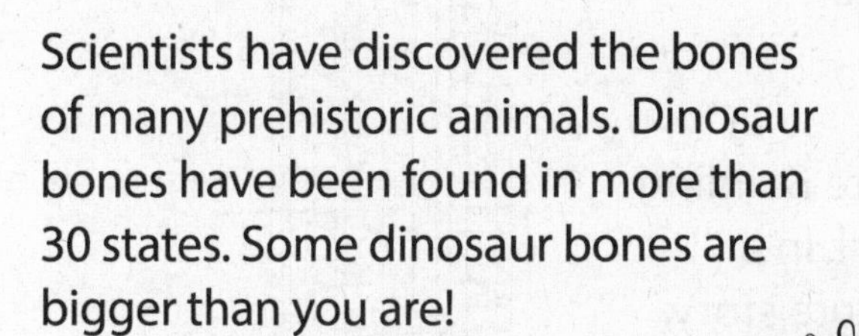

Scientists have discovered the bones of many prehistoric animals. Dinosaur bones have been found in more than 30 states. Some dinosaur bones are bigger than you are!

Your Project Make a Poster

Read about the number of bones in different animals. Then make a poster with a title and drawings or images of at least 4 animals that you researched.

Include a table or summary that mentions:

- The names of your animals
- How many bones they have in numbers
- How many bones they have with number words
- A list ordering the animals based on the number of bones they have, from the least to the greatest

Name ______________________________

Pick a Project

Project 1B

Skyscrapers, How Big?

The term *skyscraper* originally applied to buildings with 10 to 20 stories. Now the term is generally used to describe high-rise buildings greater than 40 or 50 stories.

The Home Insurance Building in Chicago, Illinois, is recognized as the world's first skyscraper. The 10-story building was considered very tall when it was completed in 1885.

It was a new type of building that was supported by a metal frame, rather than heavy stone.

The Empire State Building is 102 stories tall. In a thrilling adventure story, an apelike monster, King Kong, runs loose in New York City where he climbs to the top of the Empire State Building.

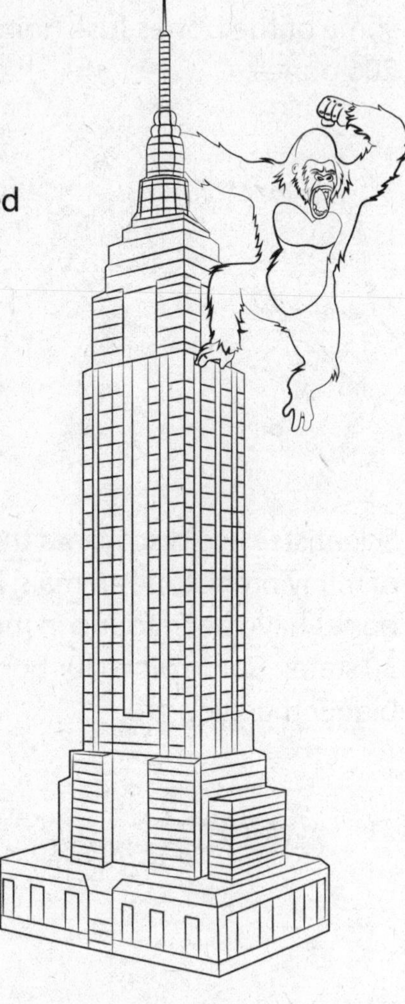

Your Project Design a Building

Find a fact sheet for a skyscraper that has 100 or more stories. Using the information on the fact sheet, write a report that includes the name of the building, where it is located, and the number of stories it has. Report on the building materials, give the amounts that are used (from the fact sheet), and describe how you think they have been used. Then pretend you are in charge of the materials for the construction of a new building. Write a fact sheet on the materials for the new building. Don't forget to sign your report and give yourself a title.

Name ____________________

Pick a Project

Project 1C

Stadium Seating Capacity

Baseball, football, hockey, and basketball are some fan favorite sports to watch in person at a stadium. The stadiums often times are shared by more than one sports team. Stadiums can be indoor, outdoor, or both indoor and outdoor because it has a retractable roof! Stadiums also host other venues such as concerts, ice shows, and other forms of entertainment.

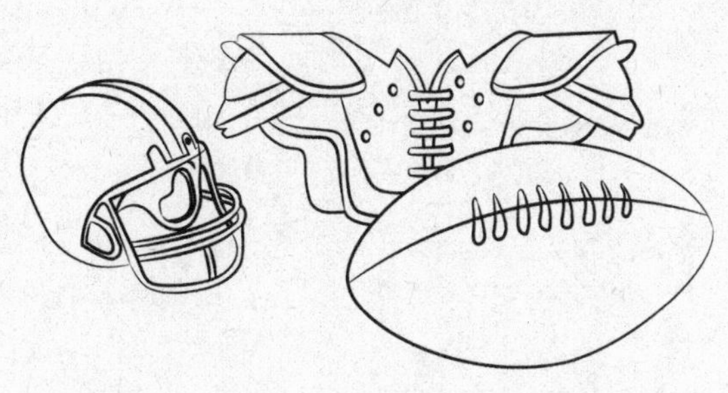

The Chicago Cubs play at Wrigley field which has a seating capacity of 41,649. The Dallas Cowboy's football team plays at AT&T Stadium, which has a seating capacity of 100,000. New York's hockey team, the New York Rangers play at Madison Square Gardens. The seating capacity for ice hockey there is 18,006. The Boston Celtics play at TD Garden which has a seating capacity of 19,580.

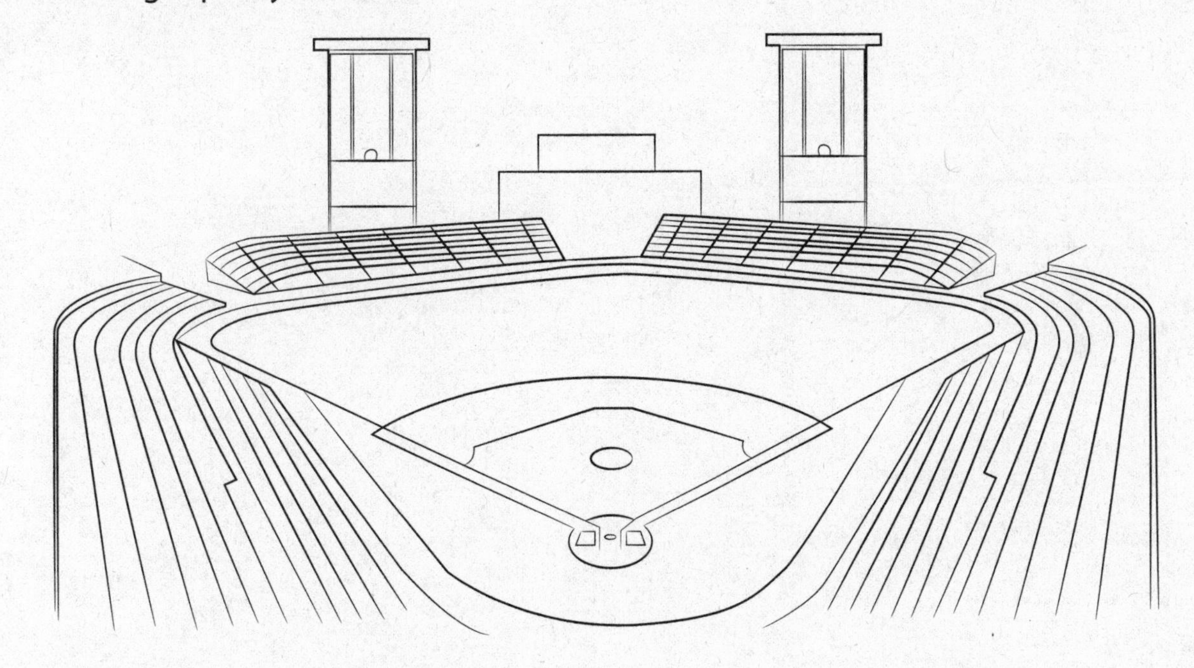

Your Project Create a Stadium Model

Create a model of one team's stadium. Make a tag that shows the name of the stadium, which team plays (or teams play) there, and how many seats it has (capacity). Research the capacity of three other stadiums for the same sport, and compare the number of seats to the stadium you chose to model.

Name ____________________

Mountain Formation

Did You Know? The Earth's crust is made up of large plates called tectonic plates. The plates keep moving a few centimeters every year. Some mountains form along the boundaries where the tectonic plates move towards each other. The tectonic plates collide, causing the Earth's crust to uplift and form mountains.

The table shows the approximate elevation of some of the tallest mountains in the world.

Mountain	Elevation (ft)
Mount Everest	29,029
K2	28,251
Kangchenjunga	28,169
Lhotse	27,940
Makalu	27,838

1. Write the elevation of Mount Everest in the place-value chart.

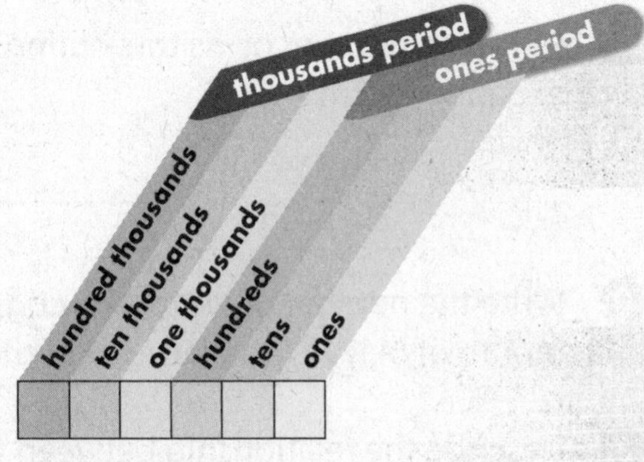

2. Write the elevation of K2 in expanded form.

____

____

3. Which mountain has an elevation of twenty-seven thousand, eight hundred thirty-eight feet?

____

4. Write the number name for the elevation of Kangchenjunga.

____

5. **Extension** Write the number name for the elevation of Lhotse. Then write the elevation in expanded form.

____

____

Name ____________________

Powerful Water

Did You Know? Grand Canyon National Park is in Arizona. The canyon is 277 miles long, stretches 18 miles at its widest point, and is about 6,000 feet deep! The Colorado River runs through the Grand Canyon. The water from the river has eroded the sides of the Grand Canyon. While the Grand Canyon is neither the widest, longest, nor deepest canyon, it is a popular tourist destination. The table shows the number of visitors by month during a recent year.

Grand Canyon Visitors

Month	Number of Visitors
April	375,899
May	468,178
June	613,479
July	728,543
August	633,026

1. Write the number of visitors during the month of April in expanded form.

2. Write the number of visitors during the month of May in the place-value chart.

3. Describe the relationship between the values of the 3s in the number of visitors during the month of August.

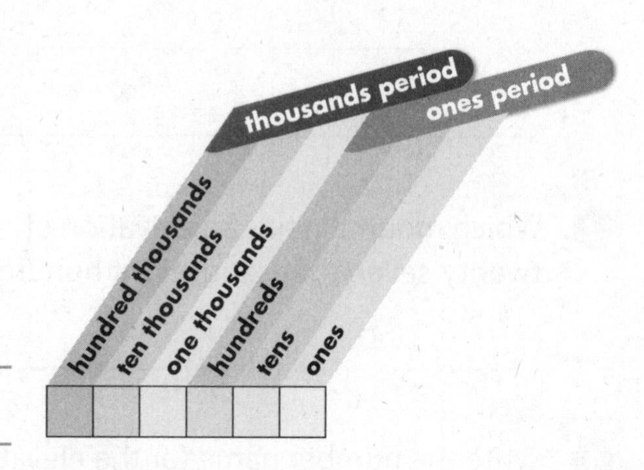

4. **Extension** During the month of May, 468,178 people visited the park. Is the value of the 8 in the thousands place ten times as great as the value of the 8 in the ones place? Explain.

Name ______________________________

Daily Review
1-1

1. Celia used an addition expression to find 6×5. Which expression did Celia use?

Ⓐ $5 + 5 + 5$

Ⓑ $5 + 5 + 5 + 5$

Ⓒ $5 + 5 + 5 + 5 + 5 + 5$

Ⓓ $5 + 5 + 5 + 5 + 5 + 5 + 5$

2. John cut some wood into 2 pieces, each 9 yards long. What was the length of the wood before it was cut?

Ⓐ 22 yards

Ⓑ 19 yards

Ⓒ 18 yards

Ⓓ $2\frac{1}{3}$ yards

3. Select all of the rectangles that have an area of 24 square centimeters.

☐ 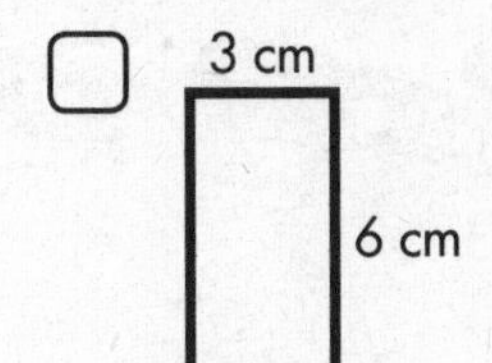

☐ 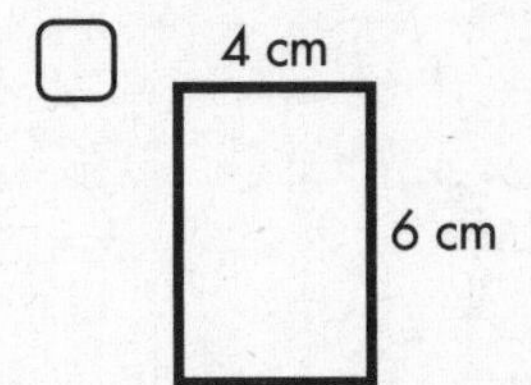

☐ 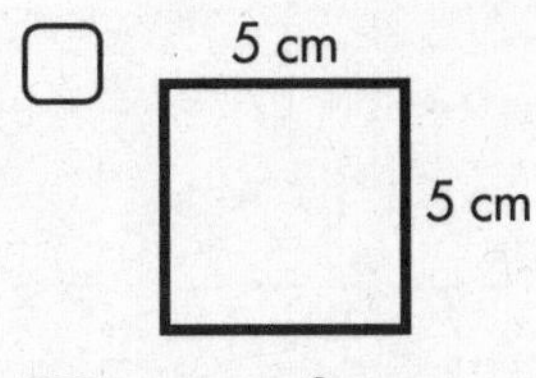

☐ 8 cm × 3 cm

☐ 12 cm × 2 cm

4. The Perez family is driving to visit relatives. The trip is 184 miles, and they have driven 48 miles. How many more miles do they need to drive?

____

5. Colton builds a sandbox for his cousin. The sandbox measures 4 feet by 3 feet. What is the perimeter of the sandbox?

____

6. Five people bought raffle tickets. They bought 8 tickets each. How many raffle tickets did they buy in all?

____

7. Una put the same number of carnations into 4 vases. If she used a total of 32 carnations, how many carnations are in each vase?

____

8. Multiply.

$4 \times 40 =$ ______

9. What number makes both equations true?

$6 \times \square = 36$

$36 \div \square = 6$

______

Name ____________________

Vocabulary

1. Each **period** of a place-value chart has three places.
   Which periods are shown in the place-value chart at the right?

   ____

   ____

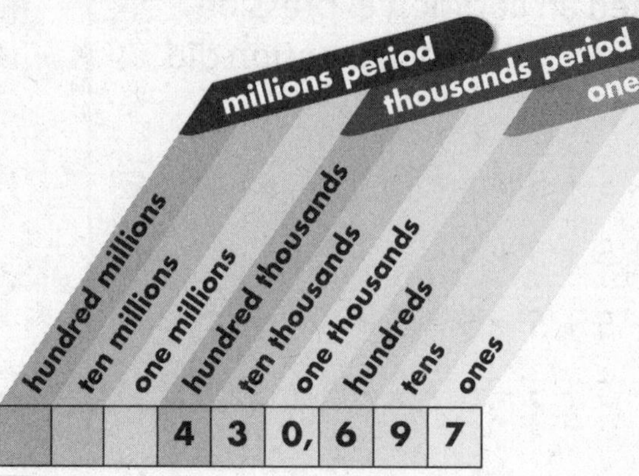

2. The position of a digit in a number tells the value of the digit. This is called **place value**.

   What is the value of the 6 in 430,697?

   ____

3. The **expanded form** of a number shows the sum of the value of each digit in a number.

   Use the place-value chart to help write 430,697 in expanded form.

   ____

4. Write 656,132 in the place-value chart to the right.

5. Write 656,132 in expanded form.

   ____

   ____

   ____

millions period | thousands period | ones period

hundred millions | ten millions | one millions | hundred thousands | ten thousands | one thousands | hundreds | tens | ones

On the Back!

6. According to the 2010 census, the population of 20-24 year olds in Alabama was 335,322. Draw a place-value chart and record 335,322. Then write 335,322 in expanded form.

Name ______________________________

Build Mathematical Literacy
1-1

Read the problem. Answer the questions to help understand the problem.

Jessica wants to buy a new team jacket that costs $35. If Jessica saves $5 a week for 4 weeks and $4 a week for 3 weeks, will she have enough money to buy the team jacket?

Preview: Read the problem through once.

1. Can the problem be answered in one step?

____

2. What question will the final step answer?

____

____

3. Underline the important facts in the problem.

____

4. What should be calculated first?

____

____

5. What operation do you use when you find the total?

____

6. How do you know if Jessica has enough money to buy the team jacket?

____

Name ______________________

Changing Places

Look at the chart. Something has happened to the *place value* of each starting number. Write the part that is missing in each row. Use the sample to help you.

	Starting Number	Place Value Change	Ending Number
Sample:	1,426	2 tens *less*	1,406
1.	73,458	3 thousands *more*	
2.		5 ones *less*	496,350
3.	91,858		91,758
4.	8,537	6 tens *more*	
5.		4 hundred thousands *more*	754,311
6.	172,618		102,618
7.	342		9,342
8.		1 ten *less*	254,008
9.	121,021	11 tens *more*	
10.	594,637	1 ten thousand *more*	
11.		3 thousands *less*	723,432
12.	99,999		100,009

Name ____________________

1. Which of the following is the number name for 564?

Ⓐ five hundred sixty-six
Ⓑ five hundred sixty-four
Ⓒ five hundred sixty
Ⓓ five hundred forty-six

2. A restaurant cuts its large pizzas into 8 equal pieces. How many total pieces of pizza will be cut for 9 large pizzas?

Ⓐ 72 pieces
Ⓑ 60 pieces
Ⓒ 45 pieces
Ⓓ 27 pieces

3. Margaret is painting one wall in her room. The wall is 7 feet long and 8 feet high. What is the area of the wall Margaret is painting?

Ⓐ 14 square feet
Ⓑ 15 square feet
Ⓒ 30 square feet
Ⓓ 56 square feet

4. Select all of the equations with an even product.

☐ $2 \times 9 = n$
☐ $5 \times 9 = n$
☐ $4 \times 5 = n$
☐ $1 \times 6 = n$
☐ $7 \times 7 = n$

5. Dean travels 12 miles to get to work. Lisa travels 9 miles less than Dean travels to get to work. Pam travels twice as far as Lisa to get to work. How many miles does Pam travel to get to work?

____

6. What number makes each equation true?

$3 \times \square = 12$

$\square \times 3 = 12$

$12 \div 3 = \square$

$12 \div \square = 3$

____

7. Round 348 to the nearest hundred.

____

8. Write 4,208 in expanded form.

____

9. Write the number name for 21,379.

____

____

____

Name ____________________

Vocabulary

1. When two **digits** next to each other in a number are the same, the value of the digit on the left is always ten times as great as the value of the digit on the right.

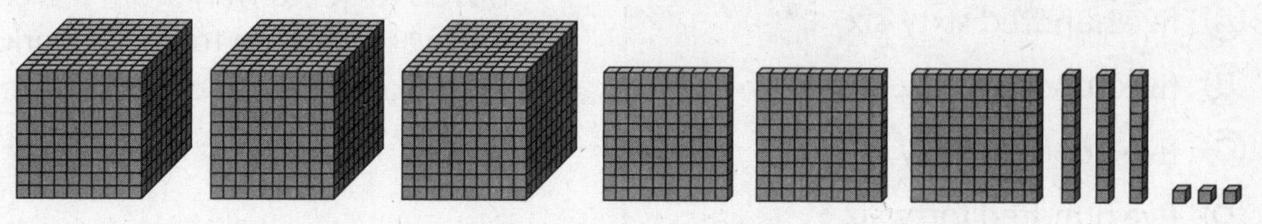

What number is represented in the model above?

____

2. The first 3 in <u>3</u>,333 is the thousands place. What is the value of the first 3? ____________

3. The second 3 in 3,<u>3</u>33 is in the hundreds place. What is the value of the second 3? ____________

4. What is the relationship between the value of the first 3 and the value of the second 3 in <u>3,3</u>33?

The value of the first 3 is ____________ times as great as the value of the second 3.

5. Complete these sentences.
In 5,550, the second 5 is in the hundreds place.

Its value is ____________.

The third 5 is in the ____________ place.

Its value is ____________.

The value of the 5 in the ____________ place is ten times as great as the value of the 5 in the ____________ place.

On the Back!

6. Describe the relationship between the 2s in 75,222.

Name ______________________________

Read the problem. Answer the questions to help understand the problem.

Describe two ways to find the area of the shaded rectangle.

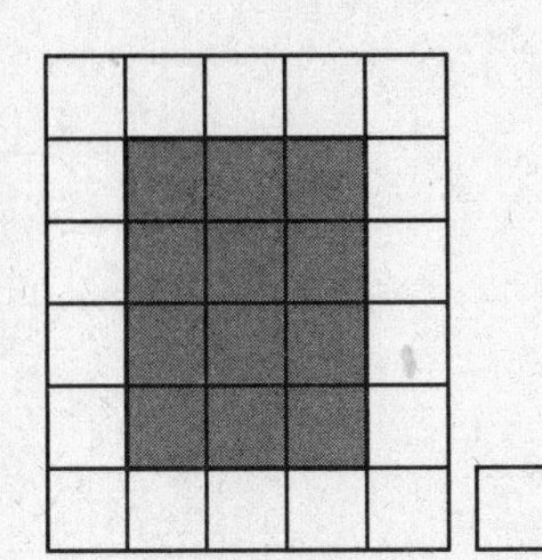

= 1 square unit

1. What is area?

____

2. Will your answer be a number?

____

____

3. What information does the key to the right of the shaded grid give you?

____

4. What part of the image will you use to find the area?

____

5. What is one way to find the area of the shaded rectangle?

____

6. What is another way to find the area of the shaded rectangle?

____

Name ______________________

Enrichment **1-2**

Place-Value Relationships

In multi-digit numbers, when the same two digits are next to each other, the value of the digit at the left is ten times greater than the value of the digit at the right. For example:

$$99 = 90 + 9$$

$$9 \text{ ones} \times 10 = 90$$

When the same two digits are separated by one digit, the value of the digit at the left is one hundred times greater than the value of the digit at the right. For example:

$$909 = 900 + 9$$

$$9 \text{ ones} \times 100 = 900$$

When the same two digits are separated by two digits, the value of the digit at the left is one thousand times greater than the value of the digit at the right. For example:

$$9{,}009 = 9{,}000 + 9$$

$$9 \text{ ones} \times 1{,}000 = 9{,}000$$

Name the values of the given digits in each number. Then tell how many times greater the value of the digit at the left is than the value of the digit at the right.

1. the 3s in 330 ________ ________ How many times greater? ________

2. the 2s in 202 ________ ________ How many times greater? ________

3. the 6s in 6,600 ________ ________ How many times greater? ________

4. the 1s in 1,001 ________ ________ How many times greater? ________

5. the 8s in 8,485 ________ ________ How many times greater? ________

6. the 4s in 400,400 ________ ________ How many times greater? ________

7. the 4s in 346,754 ________ ________ How many times greater? ________

8. the 3s in 300,003 ________ ________ How many times greater? ________

Name ______________________________

Daily Review

1-3

1. Which place has the least value in 2,387?

Ⓐ thousands place

Ⓑ hundreds place

Ⓒ tens place

Ⓓ ones place

2. Which is 3,072 written in expanded form?

Ⓐ 300 + 70 + 2

Ⓑ 3,000 + 70 + 2

Ⓒ 3,000 + 700 + 2

Ⓓ 3,000 + 700 + 20

3. Which number is equivalent to $\frac{8}{8}$?

Ⓐ $\frac{4}{3}$

Ⓑ 1

Ⓒ $\frac{1}{2}$

Ⓓ 0

4. The model below shows a number. Select all the ways the number can be written.

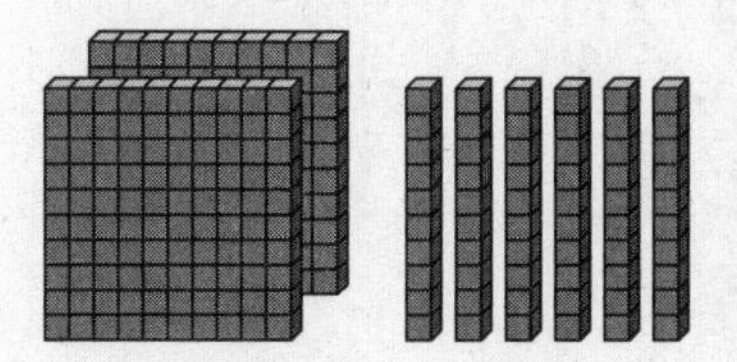

☐ 2,069

☐ 2,000 + 60 + 9

☐ 300 + 60 + 9

☐ 269

☐ two hundred sixty-nine

5. The table shows the number of cars sold each month.

Month	Cars Sold
April	589
May	523
June	651

How many more cars were sold in June than April?

____

6. Timothy's swim practice started at 2:45 P.M. and ended at 4:00 P.M. How long was his swim practice?

____

7. Stephanie had 22 marbles. She gave Maggie and Sam each 4 marbles. Explain how you can find how many marbles Stephanie has left.

____

____

____

____

____

____

Name ____________________

Reteach to Build Understanding
1-3

Vocabulary

1. The **greater than symbol (>)** is used to show the number to the left of the symbol has a greater value than the number to the right of the symbol.

   Use the greater than symbol to compare 28 and 23. __________

2. The **less than symbol (<)** is used to show the number to the left of the symbol has a lesser value than the number to the right of the symbol.

   Use the less than symbol to compare 28 and 23. __________

Use the place-value chart to compare 263,961 and 265,340. Begin comparing at the left.

3. What is the value of the 2 in both numbers? the 6 in both numbers?

   ____

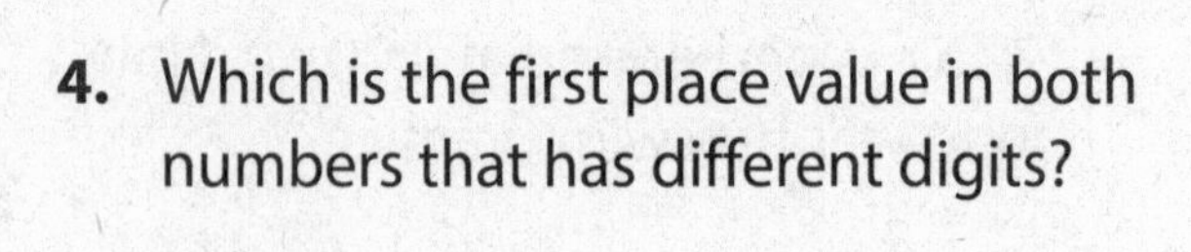

4. Which is the first place value in both numbers that has different digits?

   ____

thousands period			ones period		
hundred thousands	ten thousands	one thousands	hundreds	tens	ones
2	6	3,	9	6	1
2	6	5,	3	4	0

5. The number with the greater digit in the ____________________ is the greater number. Use the greater than symbol to compare the numbers.

   ____

Use the place-value chart to answer the questions.

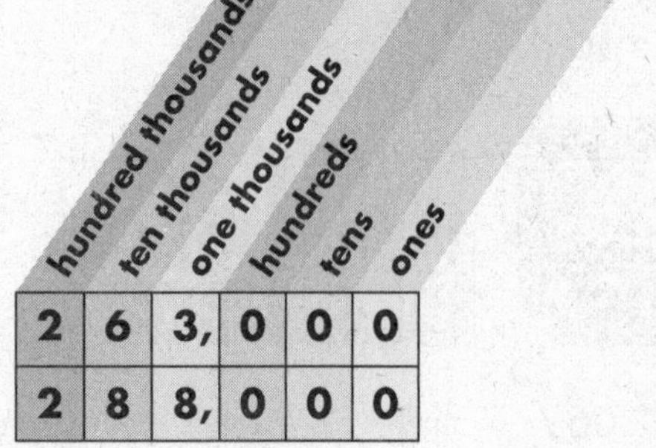

6. Which is the greater number?

   ____

7. Which is the lesser number?

   ____

On the Back!

8. Write three comparisons using the numbers below.

   34,930 34,390 34,093

Name ______________________________

Read the problem. Answer the questions to help understand the problem.

Write three numbers for which you would use the hundreds place to compare to 35,712.

1. When you compare numbers, what symbols do you use?

2. What numbers are you comparing in this problem?

3. Which digit is in the hundreds place of 35,712?

4. Explain what it means to use the hundreds place to compare to 35,712.

5. What digits can you use in the hundreds place?

6. Will the digits you write in the tens place and the ones place affect the numbers you write? Explain your answer.

Name ______________________

Enrichment
1-3

Follow the Leader

Find the path to the finish line. You can only travel to a greater number. You cannot move diagonally. Color the boxes as you find your way.

Start

1	0	3	17,642	7	1,543	3,839	1,848	4,699
17	35	34	183	1,572	2,600	3,847	3,849	4,722
6	56	15	205	206	1,955	842	3,763	7,026
31	89	37	207	444	701	83	10,303	8,103
62	103	112	150	305	697	98	11,001	8,100
17	59	97	3	9,621	14	19,423	15,211	12,964
12,043	703	84	12,652	30,654	19,342	19,464	1,643	1,673
1,334	945	3	7,003	632	948	21,190	23,023	25,901

Finish

Name ______________________________

Daily Review
1-4

1. Which is twenty thousand, eight hundred twelve written with base-ten numerals?

Ⓐ 28,012
Ⓑ 20,812
Ⓒ 2,812
Ⓓ 2,012

2. Pat drove 539 miles on a trip. What is the number of miles rounded to the nearest hundred?

Ⓐ 700 miles
Ⓑ 600 miles
Ⓒ 540 miles
Ⓓ 500 miles

3. What is the perimeter of a square that is 3 inches on one side?

Ⓐ 15 inches
Ⓑ 12 inches
Ⓒ 9 inches
Ⓓ 3 inches

4. Which of the shapes listed below can also be named a parallelogram? Select all that apply.

☐ square
☐ triangle
☐ rectangle
☐ rhombus
☐ polygon

5. Which place value do you use to compare the numbers?

145,525
145,552

____

6. Use base-ten numerals to write the number shown by the model below.

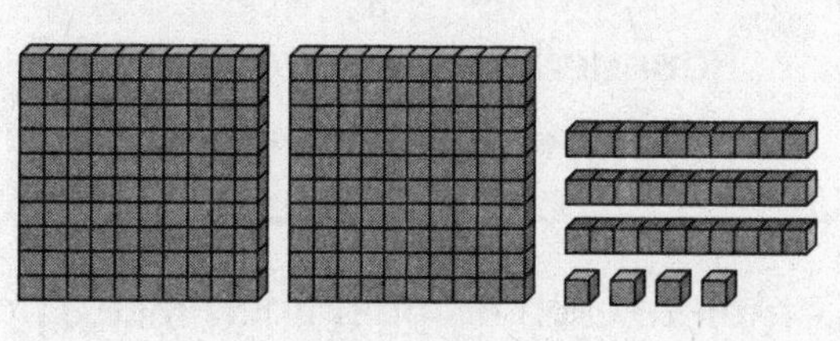

____

7. Yul tossed a coin 10 times and recorded the results in the bar graph below.

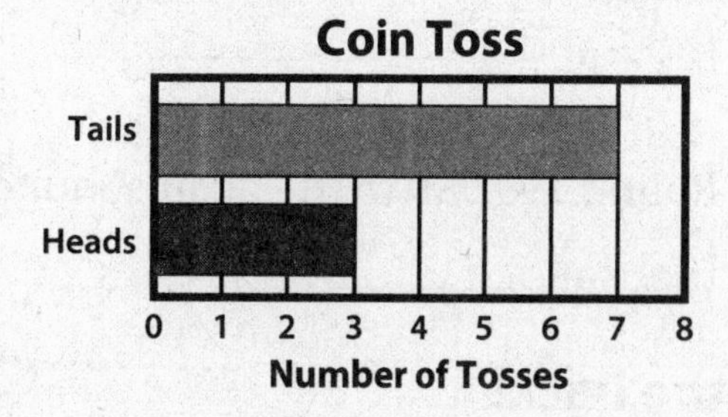

How many more times did the coin come up tails than heads?

____

8. Compare. Use <, >, or =.

39 ◯ 40

Name ____________________

Reteach to Build Understanding
1-4

Vocabulary

1. **Rounding** is a way to find which multiple of 10, 100, or 1,000, and so on, a number is closest to.

   First mark the two multiples of 1,000 that 3,567 is between.

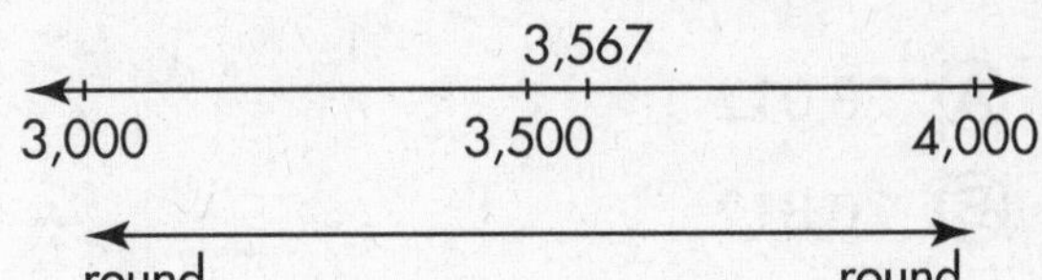

   Next find the halfway point between the two multiples, 3,000 and 4,000.

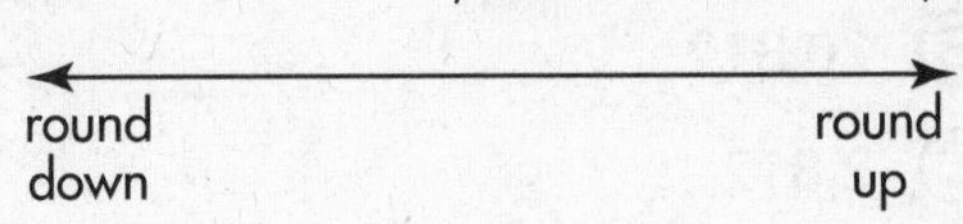

   Is 3,567 to the right or to the left of the halfway point? ____________

   Rounded to the nearest thousand, 3,567 rounds to ____________.

Complete each number line. Place a point on the number line where the number you are rounding is. Then round.

2. Round 392,153 to the nearest ten. ____________

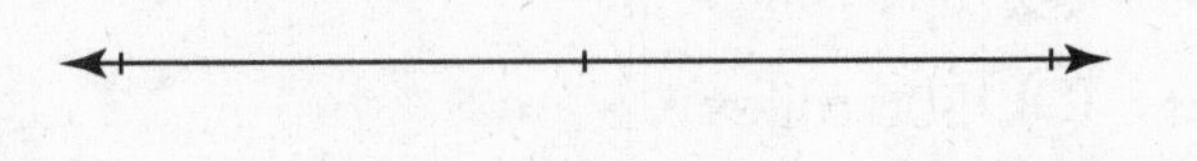

3. Round 29,485 to the nearest thousand. ____________

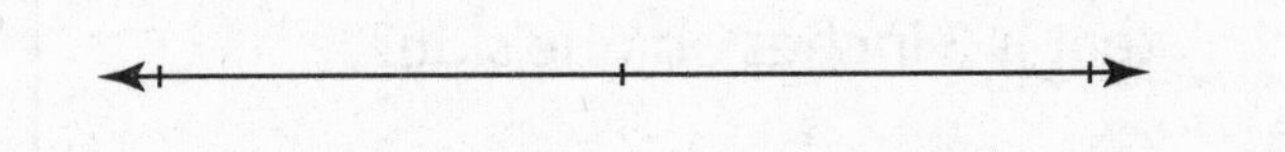

4. Round 199,999 to the nearest hundred thousand. ____________

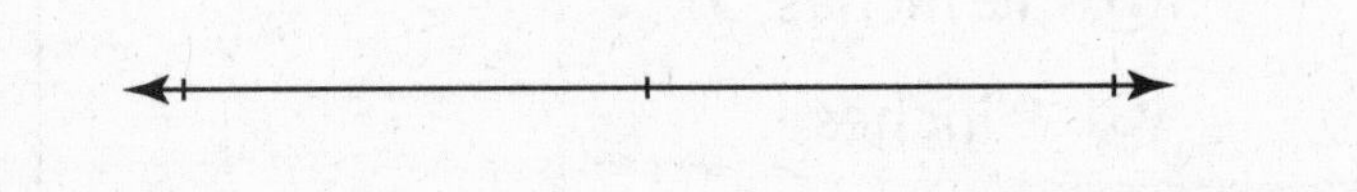

On the Back!

5. Round 592,655 to the nearest hundred thousand, ten thousand, and thousand.

6. Write three numbers that round to 400.

Name ______________________________

Build Mathematical Literacy
1-4

Read the problem. Answer the questions to help understand the problem.

Liz attended class every day since she started school as a kindergartner. She said she has been in school for about 1,000 days. What numbers could be the actual number of school days if Liz rounded to the nearest ten?

1. Does the sentence, *Liz attended class every day since she started school as a kindergartner.* contain all of the information that is needed to answer this question?

____

2. What does the phrase *about 1,000 days* tell you about the number 1,000?

____

____

3. Is there only one number needed to answer this problem?

____

____

4. What do the numbers you answer with need to round to?

____

5. What place value are you rounding to in this problem?

____

6. What tool can you use to help answer this problem?

____

Name ___________________________

Enrichment
1-4

Rounding Around

Use the clues to find each number. Circle your choice.

1. The number rounded to the nearest thousand is 5,000. The number is greater than 4,800. The number is less than 5,000.

5,009	4,670
5,900	4,900

2. The number rounded to the nearest thousand is 1,000. The number is less than 1,200. The sum of the digits is 4.

1,508	1,489
1,111	964

3. The number rounded to the nearest thousand is 20,000. The number is less than 20,100. The number is between 19,500 and 20,000.

19,055	20,080
20,399	19,671

4. The number rounded to the nearest ten is 48,500. The number has a 4 in the hundreds place. The ones digit is odd.

48,395	8,499
48,495	48,496

5. The number has 5 digits. The number rounded to the nearest ten thousand is 40,000. The number is odd.

36,456	37,022
137,220	36,943

6. The number rounded to the nearest hundred thousand is 400,000. The number is 100 times greater than 3,700.

3,800	400,100
370,000	401,111

7. The number rounded to the nearest hundred and to the nearest thousand is 845,000. The value of the digit in the hundred thousands place is 100,000 times as great as the value of the digit in the ones place.

844,378	844,978
844,987	844,975

Name ______________________

Daily Review
1-5

1. In 2012, about five hundred seventy-six thousand, four hundred twelve people lived in Wyoming. Which shows this number using base-ten numerals?

Ⓐ 507,612
Ⓑ 567,412
Ⓒ 576,412
Ⓓ 577,612

2. Which rounds to 70,000 when rounding to the nearest thousand?

Ⓐ 71,682
Ⓑ 70,592
Ⓒ 69,823
Ⓓ 69,384

3. Nick has 700 baseball cards. He gives 374 to his younger sister. How many baseball cards does Nick have now?

Ⓐ 226 baseball cards
Ⓑ 276 baseball cards
Ⓒ 326 baseball cards
Ⓓ 436 baseball cards

4. In which numbers is the value of the underlined digit ten times as great as the value of the circled digit?

- ☐ <u>6</u>67,7⑥7
- ☐ ⑥<u>6</u>7,767
- ☐ <u>6</u>⑥7,767
- ☐ 66<u>7</u>,⑦67
- ☐ 667,<u>7</u>6⑦

5. What is 549,423 rounded to the nearest thousand?

____

6. Nina has 465 pennies in a jar. Daryl has 348 pennies in a jar. How many pennies do they have in all?

____

7. The table shows how many marbles four friends have in their collections.

Marble Collections

Friend	Number of Marbles
Sven	580
Rita	572
Wendy	610
Carlos	602

Compare the number of marbles Rita has to the number of marbles Carlos has. Write a comparison using >, =, or <.

____

____

8. Write the number name for 45,391.

____

____

Name ____________________

Vocabulary

1. You can **construct an argument** to support or oppose a conjecture. A **conjecture** is a statement that is thought to be true but has not yet been proven.

When you construct an argument, give a clear and complete explanation, and use numbers, objects, drawings, or actions to justify your argument.

The land area of Texas is two hundred sixty-one thousand, two hundred thirty-two square miles. The number is written as 261,332. Construct a math argument that explains if the number is written correctly.

____

____

____

Use the information in the **Area of Texas Cities** table to construct math arguments to explain if the conjectures are correct or incorrect.

Area of Texas Cities

City	Area (square kilometers)
Austin	704
Dallas	999
Fort Worth	904
Houston	1,625

2. Conjecture: Fort Worth has a greater area than Austin.

____

____

____

3. Conjecture: The 9 in the hundreds place in Dallas's area is ten times as great as the 9 in the ones place of its area.

____

____

On the Back!

4. The water area of Texas is seven thousand, three hundred sixty-five square miles. The number is written 7,365. Construct a math argument that explains if the number is written correctly or not.

Name ______________________________

Read the problem. Answer the questions to help understand the problem.

The planets in our solar system are different sizes, as shown below. Nora conjectured that Jupiter's equator is about 10 times as long as Earth's equator. What are the possible estimates for the lengths of the equators of Jupiter and Earth?

Length of Equators for 4 Planets

Earth 40,030 km

Jupiter 439,264 km

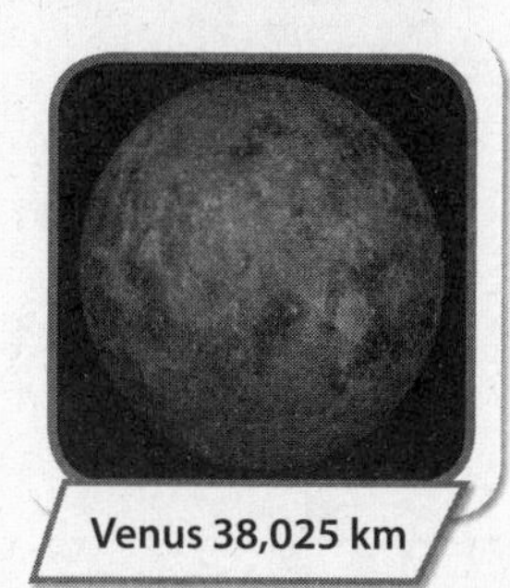
Venus 38,025 km

Mars 21,297 km

1. What is a conjecture?

____

____

2. Do you use all 4 lengths of the equators to answer this question?

____

____

3. Do you use the numbers as labeled below Earth and Jupiter?

____

____

4. What do you need to do to estimate the lengths?

____

5. Have you answered the question after you estimate the lengths?

____

____

Name ______________________________

Skipping with Numbers

Follow the directions to write each number.

1. Skip count 3 times by hundreds.
   Skip count 2 times by tens.
   There is a 9 in the ones place.
   The number is __________.

2. There are 40 thousands.
   There are 40 tens.
   There are 3 ones.
   The number is __________.

3. Skip count 5 times by ten thousand.
   Skip count 8 times by hundreds.
   Skip count 8 times by tens.
   The number is __________.

4. There are 60 ten thousands.
   There are 20 thousands.
   There are 9 tens.
   There are 9 ones.
   The number is __________.

5. Skip count 10 times by thousands.
   There are 20 hundreds.
   Skip count 8 times by hundreds.
   Skip count 3 times by tens.
   There are 6 ones.
   The number is __________.

6. There are 3 hundred thousands.
   There are 70 ten thousands.
   The number is __________.

Name ______________________________

Fluently Add and Subtract Multi-Digit Whole Numbers

Dear Family,

Your child is learning to fluently add and subtract multi-digit whole numbers. Rounding is used to find values that are close to a correct answer. Rounding is a useful skill to check if an answer is reasonable. For example, if you buy two pairs of pants for $18 each, the total should be about $40. If you get a very different answer, then you probably calculated incorrectly. Your child will apply this same logic to numbers greater than or equal to 1,000.

Your child will get a lot of practice doing "mental math," either by using addition properties or by using strategies such as counting on and compensation. The activity below is an example of the types of problems your child will solve in this topic.

Estimate the Total

Materials paper and pencil

Look through the car sales section of your local newspaper. Have your child select two vehicles he or she would like to purchase. Ask your child to round the price of each car to the nearest thousand. Have your child estimate the total cost for both cars using the rounded values. Repeat the steps for additional pairs of vehicle prices.

Observe Your Child

Ask your child to write a general statement explaining how he or she estimated the costs of the items.

Nombre ________________________________

Sumar y restar números de varios dígitos con facilidad

Estimada familia:

Su niño(a) está aprendiendo a sumar y restar números de varios dígitos con facilidad. Redondear se usa para hallar valores cercanos a la respuesta correcta. Redondear es una destreza útil para comprobar si una respuesta es razonable. Por ejemplo, si usted compra dos pares de pantalones a $ 18 cada uno, el total debería ser aproximadamente $ 40. Si obtiene una respuesta muy diferente, probablemente se deba a que calculó incorrectamente. Su niño(a) va a aplicar esta misma lógica a números más grandes o iguales a 1,000.

Su niño(a) va a practicar mucho el "cálculo mental", usando tanto propiedades de la suma como estrategias como el conteo o la compensación. La siguiente actividad es un ejemplo de los tipos de problemas que su niño(a) va a resolver en este tema.

Estimar el total

Materiales papel y lápiz

Observe la sección de venta de carros en su periódico local. Pida a su niño(a) que seleccione dos carros que le gustaría comprar. Pídale que redondee el precio de cada carro al millar más cercano. Pídale que estime el costo total que van a tener los dos carros usando los valores redondeados. Repita los pasos con otros pares de carros.

Observe a su niño(a)

Pídale que escriba un enunciado general para explicar cómo estimó el costo de los objetos.

Name ______________________________

Pick a Project

Project 2A

Population

Florida is the third most populated of the 50 states in the United States. In 2015, Florida had a population of more than 20,000,000 people. Only California and Texas have more residents than Florida.

Jacksonville has a population of more than 860,000 people and has the largest population of all cities in Florida.

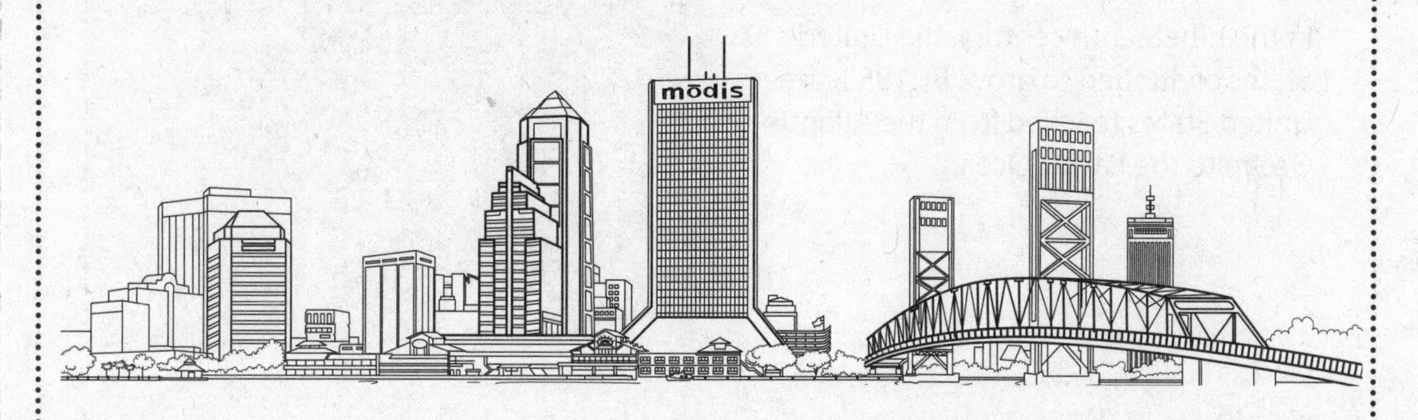

Your Project Map the Population of Your State's Largest Cities

Find the populations of the 4 largest cities in your state. Then on a map of your state, find and label the locations of each of these cities. Compare the populations of each of the four cities, and then list the populations in order from greatest to least.

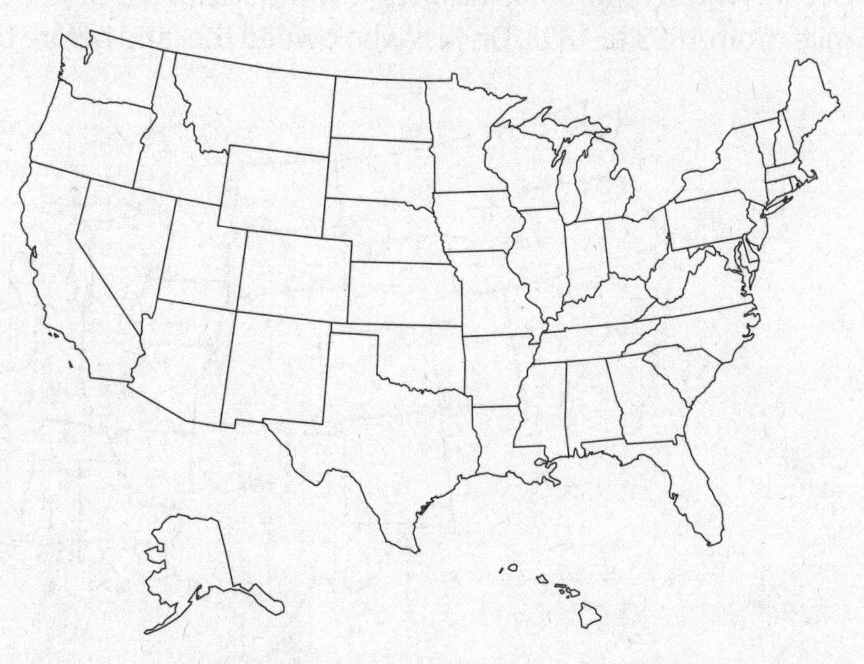

Name ______________________________

Growth of the United States

The United States did not always reach from the Atlantic Ocean to the Pacific Ocean. The original 13 colonies only went as far west as western Florida. As part of the Treaty of Paris in 1783, the United States reached as far west as the Mississippi River.

In the nineteenth century, the United States continued to grow. By 1853, the United States reached from the Atlantic Ocean to the Pacific Ocean.

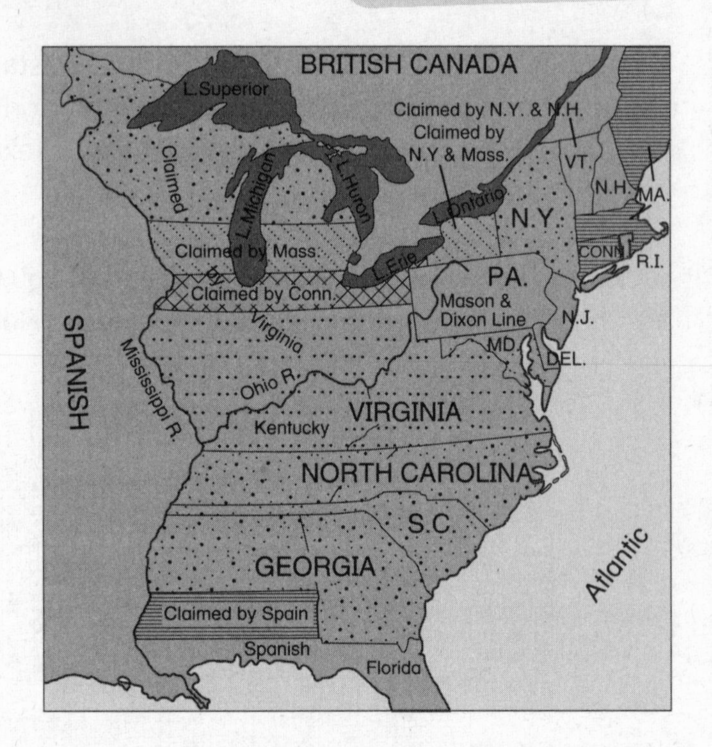

Your Project Write a Report on U.S. Expansion

Research the events that led to the United States reaching from the Atlantic to the Pacific Ocean. Write a report that includes how the size of the United States increased in square miles from 1803 to 1853. Discuss who owned the land before the United States acquired it.

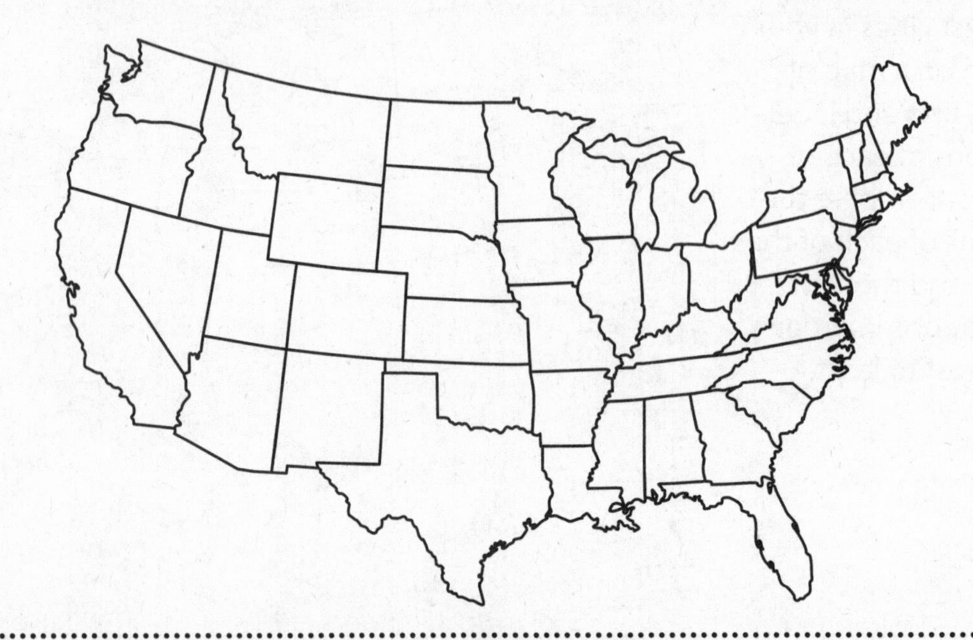

Name ___

Pick a Project

Project 2C

The Planets

Our solar system consists of the Sun and eight planets. The planets all revolve around the Sun. Each planet's year is the length of time it takes the planet to complete one revolution around the Sun.

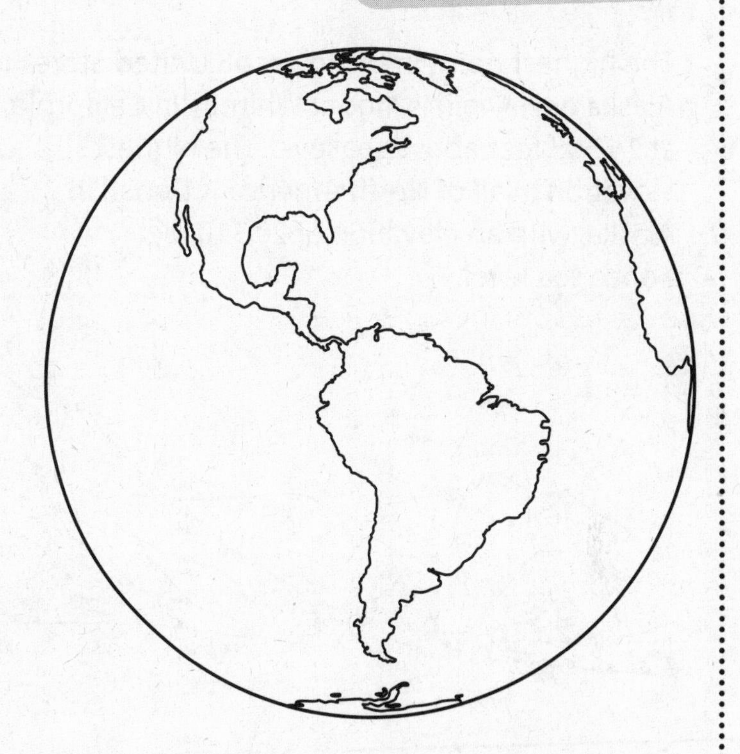

A year on Mercury is about 88 Earth days and a year on Neptune is about 165 Earth years.

The planets are different sizes. The size of a planet can be determined by its radius. The radius of a planet is the distance from the planet's exact center to its surface.

Your Project Make a Model of the Solar System

Research the sizes of the planets and the Sun. Make a model of the Sun and the eight planets. Write information about each planet, including the radius of each. Choose a planet that is larger than Earth and a planet that is smaller than Earth. Find the difference between the radius of Earth and the radius of the larger planet and the difference between the radius of Earth and the radius of the smaller planet.

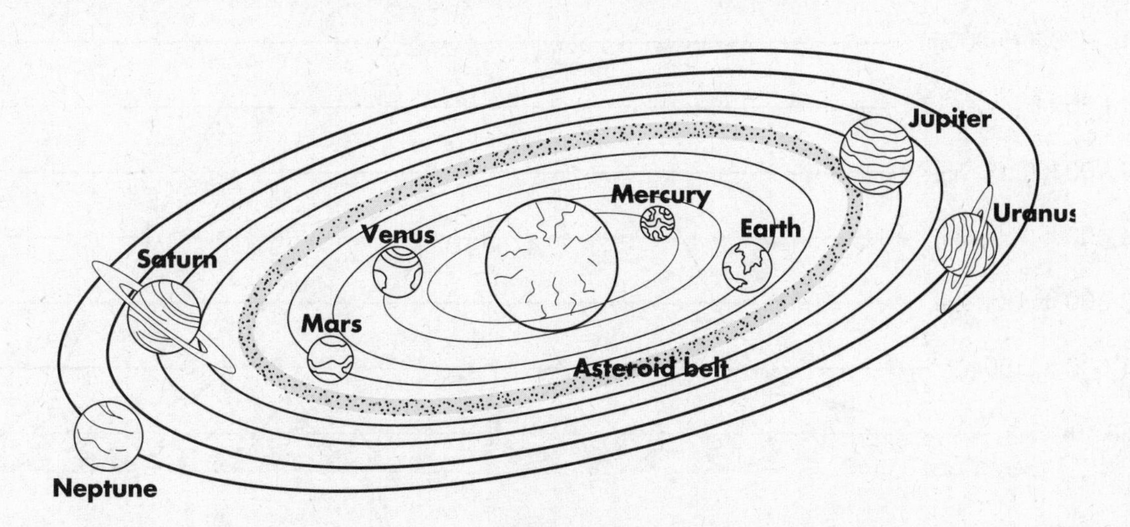

Name ______________________

Pick a Project

Project 2D

Climbing Mountains

The highest point in the lower 48 United States (not including Alaska or Hawaii) is Mount Whitney in California, at 14,505 feet above sea level. The highest elevation in all of North America is Denali in Alaska, with an elevation of 20,310 feet above sea level.

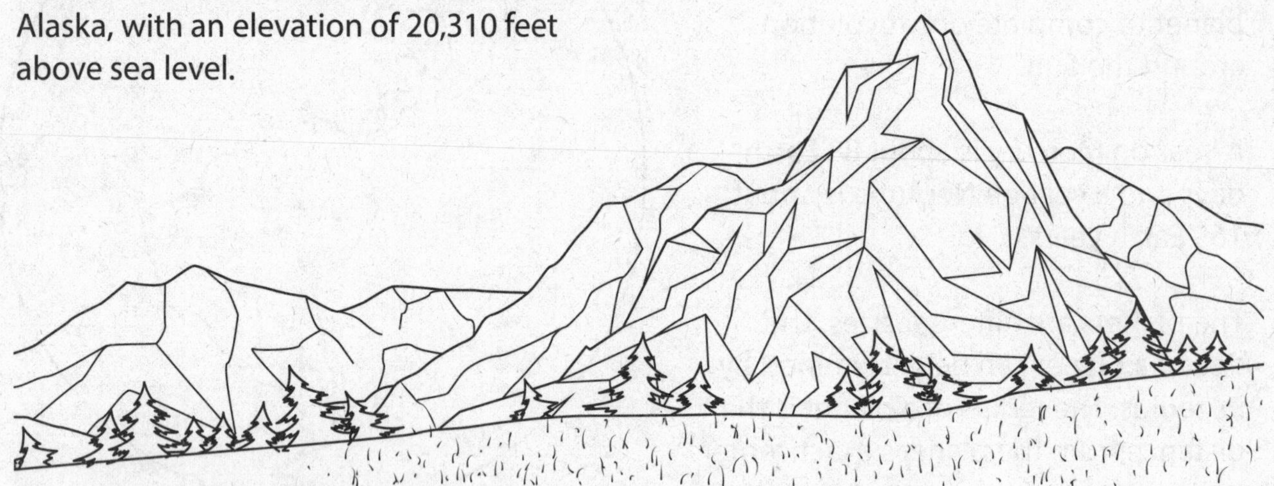

Your Project Compare Mountain Elevations

Research and choose 10-12 mountains in the United States and/or the world. Make a table and list the names and heights of each of the mountains. Then create several word problems where the heights of the mountains are compared.

Name ______________________________

Add and Subtract Multi-Digit Whole Numbers

1. 4,216 + 310

2. 3,217 + 1,203 + 5,436

3. 82,913 + 4,306

4. 6,825 − 419

5. 92,454 − 8,321

6. 465,892 − 52,680

7. 5,628 + 439

8. 57,467 + 24,756

9. 125,936 + 283,415

10. 6,281 + 2,252 + 5,436

11. 7,283 − 4,659

12. 83,625 − 4,307

13. 124,248 − 55,679

14. 5,903 − 429

15. 70,489 − 26,724

16. 29,084 − 3,695

17. 520,675 − 458,892

18. 9,007 − 359

19. 60,003 − 25,934

20. 902,040 − 375,281

21. Insert one digit in each box to complete the addition problem. You will not use the same digit twice.

```
  5, □ □ 5
+ 3, 4 8 □
----------
  □, 3 5 7
```

Name ______________________

Add and Subtract Multi-Digit Whole Numbers

1. $\begin{array}{r} 5{,}413 \\ +\ 2{,}371 \\ \hline \end{array}$

2. $\begin{array}{r} 6{,}076 \\ 1{,}611 \\ +\ 252 \\ \hline \end{array}$

3. $\begin{array}{r} 56{,}912 \\ +\ 684 \\ \hline \end{array}$

4. $\begin{array}{r} 5{,}859 \\ -\ 1{,}727 \\ \hline \end{array}$

5. $\begin{array}{r} 71{,}953 \\ -\ 50{,}622 \\ \hline \end{array}$

6. $\begin{array}{r} 875{,}254 \\ -\ 525{,}133 \\ \hline \end{array}$

7. $\begin{array}{r} 4{,}914 \\ +\ 2{,}718 \\ \hline \end{array}$

8. $\begin{array}{r} 62{,}419 \\ +\ 27{,}847 \\ \hline \end{array}$

9. $\begin{array}{r} 340{,}771 \\ +\ 405{,}386 \\ \hline \end{array}$

10. $\begin{array}{r} 1{,}342 \\ 9{,}170 \\ +\ 8{,}531 \\ \hline \end{array}$

11. $\begin{array}{r} 3{,}222 \\ -\ 1{,}846 \\ \hline \end{array}$

12. $\begin{array}{r} 57{,}662 \\ -\ 3{,}193 \\ \hline \end{array}$

13. $\begin{array}{r} 372{,}189 \\ -\ 91{,}268 \\ \hline \end{array}$

14. $\begin{array}{r} 1{,}340 \\ -\ 279 \\ \hline \end{array}$

15. $\begin{array}{r} 68{,}024 \\ -\ 58{,}234 \\ \hline \end{array}$

16. $\begin{array}{r} 67{,}081 \\ -\ 8{,}487 \\ \hline \end{array}$

17. $\begin{array}{r} 890{,}586 \\ -\ 113{,}273 \\ \hline \end{array}$

18. $\begin{array}{r} 4{,}200 \\ -\ 542 \\ \hline \end{array}$

19. $\begin{array}{r} 40{,}078 \\ -\ 18{,}537 \\ \hline \end{array}$

20. $\begin{array}{r} 463{,}010 \\ -\ 289{,}701 \\ \hline \end{array}$

---

21. Insert one digit in each box to complete the subtraction problem. You will not use the same digit twice.

$\begin{array}{r} 6{,}\square\,0\,1 \\ -\ 2{,}5\,\square\,4 \\ \hline \square{,}2\,3\,\square \end{array}$

Name ______________________

Add and Subtract Multi-Digit Whole Numbers

1. $\begin{array}{r} 8{,}124 \\ +\ 1{,}655 \\ \hline \end{array}$

2. $\begin{array}{r} 5{,}124 \\ 2{,}610 \\ +\ 2{,}023 \\ \hline \end{array}$

3. $\begin{array}{r} 62{,}196 \\ +\ 3{,}453 \\ \hline \end{array}$

4. $\begin{array}{r} 8{,}164 \\ -\ 942 \\ \hline \end{array}$

5. $\begin{array}{r} 82{,}953 \\ -\ 7{,}541 \\ \hline \end{array}$

6. $\begin{array}{r} 419{,}562 \\ -\ 87{,}331 \\ \hline \end{array}$

7. $\begin{array}{r} 4{,}185 \\ +\ 956 \\ \hline \end{array}$

8. $\begin{array}{r} 71{,}963 \\ +\ 15{,}638 \\ \hline \end{array}$

9. $\begin{array}{r} 615{,}963 \\ +\ 359{,}217 \\ \hline \end{array}$

10. $\begin{array}{r} 5{,}862 \\ 9{,}726 \\ +\ 2{,}178 \\ \hline \end{array}$

11. $\begin{array}{r} 5{,}771 \\ -\ 2{,}789 \\ \hline \end{array}$

12. $\begin{array}{r} 94{,}532 \\ -\ 27{,}149 \\ \hline \end{array}$

13. $\begin{array}{r} 499{,}854 \\ -\ 309{,}766 \\ \hline \end{array}$

14. $\begin{array}{r} 5{,}607 \\ -\ 537 \\ \hline \end{array}$

15. $\begin{array}{r} 80{,}645 \\ -\ 32{,}016 \\ \hline \end{array}$

16. $\begin{array}{r} 94{,}440 \\ -\ 2{,}136 \\ \hline \end{array}$

17. $\begin{array}{r} 706{,}332 \\ -\ 167{,}941 \\ \hline \end{array}$

18. $\begin{array}{r} 3{,}020 \\ -\ 1{,}401 \\ \hline \end{array}$

19. $\begin{array}{r} 90{,}650 \\ -\ 42{,}928 \\ \hline \end{array}$

20. $\begin{array}{r} 800{,}817 \\ -\ 432{,}093 \\ \hline \end{array}$

---

21. Insert one digit in each box to complete the addition problem. You will not use the same digit twice.

$\begin{array}{r} 7{,}\ 2\ \square\ 5 \\ +\ \square{,}\ \square\ 7\ \square \\ \hline 9{,}\ 3\ 8\ 4 \end{array}$

Name ______________________

Add and Subtract Multi-Digit Whole Numbers

1. $\begin{array}{r} 6{,}284 \\ +\ 1{,}704 \\ \hline \end{array}$

2. $\begin{array}{r} 4{,}302 \\ 3{,}212 \\ +\ 2{,}434 \\ \hline \end{array}$

3. $\begin{array}{r} 17{,}237 \\ +\ 8{,}641 \\ \hline \end{array}$

4. $\begin{array}{r} 7{,}753 \\ -\ 2{,}152 \\ \hline \end{array}$

5. $\begin{array}{r} 42{,}759 \\ -\ 31{,}552 \\ \hline \end{array}$

6. $\begin{array}{r} 949{,}216 \\ -\ 71{,}102 \\ \hline \end{array}$

7. $\begin{array}{r} 9{,}417 \\ +\ 774 \\ \hline \end{array}$

8. $\begin{array}{r} 38{,}472 \\ +\ 18{,}388 \\ \hline \end{array}$

9. $\begin{array}{r} 172{,}028 \\ +\ 395{,}573 \\ \hline \end{array}$

10. $\begin{array}{r} 5{,}316 \\ 7{,}834 \\ +\ 2{,}117 \\ \hline \end{array}$

11. $\begin{array}{r} 5{,}248 \\ -\ 1{,}983 \\ \hline \end{array}$

12. $\begin{array}{r} 57{,}681 \\ -\ 8{,}458 \\ \hline \end{array}$

13. $\begin{array}{r} 519{,}416 \\ -\ 68{,}562 \\ \hline \end{array}$

14. $\begin{array}{r} 8{,}081 \\ -\ 4{,}114 \\ \hline \end{array}$

15. $\begin{array}{r} 99{,}305 \\ -\ 84{,}853 \\ \hline \end{array}$

16. $\begin{array}{r} 68{,}107 \\ -\ 9{,}438 \\ \hline \end{array}$

17. $\begin{array}{r} 423{,}088 \\ -\ 375{,}098 \\ \hline \end{array}$

18. $\begin{array}{r} 8{,}060 \\ -\ 638 \\ \hline \end{array}$

19. $\begin{array}{r} 86{,}030 \\ -\ 55{,}347 \\ \hline \end{array}$

20. $\begin{array}{r} 900{,}192 \\ -\ 252{,}378 \\ \hline \end{array}$

21. Insert one digit in each box to complete the subtraction problem. You will not use the same digit twice.

$\begin{array}{r} 4{,}\square 8\square \\ -\ \square{,}889 \\ \hline 1{,}1\square 2 \end{array}$

Name ____________________

Add and Subtract Multi-Digit Whole Numbers

1. 7,325 + 626

2. 7,258 + 311 + 117

3. 30,591 + 18,246

4. 6,368 − 6,129

5. 55,849 − 2,727

6. 677,838 − 51,307

7. 2,385 + 1,958

8. 72,866 + 89,537

9. 685,276 + 278,837

10. 8,793 + 8,530 + 6,385

11. 7,319 − 6,559

12. 82,756 − 19,539

13. 451,883 − 85,095

14. 5,607 − 611

15. 38,807 − 16,847

16. 16,990 − 5,356

17. 579,460 − 223,727

18. 5,900 − 1,251

19. 90,401 − 66,129

20. 850,073 − 264,478

---

21. Insert one digit in each box to complete the addition problem. You will not use the same digit twice.

3,□ 5 4
+ 4, 8 □□
□,5 5 1

Name ______________________

Add and Subtract Multi-Digit Whole Numbers

1. 2,538 + 5,831

2. 5,031 + 1,320 + 826

3. 44,717 + 2,430

4. 2,885 − 934

5. 68,588 − 27,740

6. 459,355 − 319,241

7. 3,746 + 859

8. 61,484 + 22,967

9. 639,790 + 108,424

10. 2,445 + 2,992 + 9,288

11. 6,581 − 2,762

12. 22,446 − 4,248

13. 356,274 − 268,669

14. 3,066 − 950

15. 38,062 − 11,258

16. 80,586 − 3,627

17. 322,702 − 196,056

18. 4,006 − 655

19. 53,000 − 30,862

20. 355,400 − 171,733

---

21. Insert one digit in each box to complete the subtraction problem. You will not use the same digit twice.

8,4 0 ☐
− ☐,3 1 2
2,☐☐5

Name ______________________

Blast Off!

Did You Know? A space shuttle is made up of three main parts: the orbiter, a large external gas tank, and rocket boosters. The rocket boosters provide most of the lift during the first two minutes of the shuttle's flight. During the first two minutes, the boosters exert energy to push the shuttle into space.

During orbit, the average speed of a space shuttle is 17,350 miles per hour. That takes a lot of energy!

The table below shows the recorded speeds of four different shuttles. Use this information to answer the questions below.

Space Shuttle	Speed (miles per hour)
A	16,324
B	17,832
C	15,392
D	17,429

1. Round each speed to the nearest thousand.

____

2. Using the rounded values from Exercise 1, estimate the difference between the slowest shuttle and the fastest shuttle.

____

3. Round each speed to the nearest hundred.

____

4. Using the rounded values from Exercise 3, estimate the difference between the slowest shuttle and the fastest shuttle.

____

5. **Extension** Look at the estimated differences found in Exercises 1 and 3. Which gives the more precise estimated difference in speed? Explain.

____

____

____

Name ______________________

Roller Coaster Ride

Did You Know? Any object that is in motion has energy. The energy of motion is called kinetic energy. There are three forms of kinetic energy—vibrational, rotational, and translational. The amount of kinetic energy an object has depends on the mass and speed of the object.

The table shows the speed and amount of kinetic energy of a roller coaster at various points on a track.

Use the information from the table to answer the questions below.

	Speed (miles per hour)	**Kinetic Energy (joules)**
Point A	10	5,000
Point B	55	195,312
Point C	75	340,312
Point D	60	227,813
Point E	40	101,250

1. At which point on the track does the roller coaster have the greatest speed?

____

2. At which point on the track does the roller coaster have the greatest amount of kinetic energy?

____

3. At which point on the track does the roller coaster have the least speed?

____

4. At which point on the track does the roller coaster have the least kinetic energy?

____

5. **Extension** Jonas says when the roller coaster is traveling 70 miles per hour, the kinetic energy is 350,000 joules. Do you agree? Explain.

____

____

____

____

Name ____________________

1. Which comparison is true?

Ⓐ 284,924 > 293,820
Ⓑ 34,948 > 34,824
Ⓒ 48,681 < 48,592
Ⓓ 23,294 < 23,294

2. What is 692,041 rounded to the nearest hundred?

Ⓐ 692,100
Ⓑ 692,040
Ⓒ 692,000
Ⓓ 691,000

3. Which is fifty-eight thousand written with numerals?

Ⓐ 580,000
Ⓑ 58,000
Ⓒ 5,800
Ⓓ 580

4. For which numbers is the value of the first underlined digit ten times as great as the value of the second underlined digit? Select all that apply.

☐ 3<u>4</u>3,43<u>4</u>
☐ 3<u>3</u><u>3</u>,333
☐ 30<u>3</u>,0<u>3</u>0
☐ 131,3<u>3</u><u>3</u>
☐ 10<u>2</u>,<u>2</u>01

5. Evan has a shell collection. On Monday, he found 6 new shells. On Tuesday, he gave 9 shells to his friends. After giving the shells away, Evan had 37 shells left. How many shells did Evan have to start?

____

6. Aretha reads 3 chapters of her book each day. How many days will it take Aretha to finish the book if it has 24 chapters? Write a number sentence to solve the problem.

____

7. What is 347,492 rounded to the nearest ten thousand?

____

8. Describe the relationship of the value of the 4 in the ten thousands place to the value of the 4 in the thousands place.

344,682

____

____

____

____

____

____

Name ______________________

Reteach to Build Understanding
2-1

Vocabulary

You can use **compensation** to add and subtract with mental math. With compensation, you adjust one number to make the computation easier. Then, you adjust the other number to compensate, or make up for the change. You can do this because of the **Identity Property of Addition**.

1. What is $2 - 2$? ______

2. Does $298 + 145 + (2 - 2) = 298 + 145$? ______

3. $(298 + 2) + (145 - 2) =$ ______ $+$ ______ $=$ ______

4. So, $298 + 145 =$ ______

Fill in the blanks to find each sum or difference with compensation and mental math.

5. $462 - 317 = (462 +$ ______$) - (317 + 3)$

$=$ ______ $-$ ______ $=$ ______

6. $2{,}396 + 1{,}536 = (2{,}396 + 4) + (1{,}536 -$ ______$)$

$=$ ______ $+$ ______ $=$ ______

7. $7{,}312 - 5{,}194 = (7{,}312 +$ ______$) - (5{,}194 + 6)$

$=$ ______ $-$ ______ $=$ ______

Use compensation to add or subtract. Show your work.

8. $1{,}700 - 398$

9. $2{,}507 + 4{,}996$

On the Back!

10. Use two 4-digit numbers to write and solve an addition or a subtraction problem. Explain how to use compensation to find the sum or difference.

Name ______________________

Build Mathematical Literacy
2-1

Read the problem. Answer the questions to help understand the problem.

Conservationists weigh two Northern elephant seals. An adult seal weighs 6,600 pounds, and its pup weighs 3,847 pounds. What is their combined weight? Explain how to use mental math to solve.

1. What do you **KNOW** from the information in the problem?

2. What information do you **NOT** need to know to solve the problem?

3. **WHAT** is this problem asking you to solve? **WHAT** word gives you this clue?

4. Will you have one answer at the end, or more than one answer? Explain.

5. What different **STRATEGIES** can you use to solve this problem?

Name ______________________________

Mental Puzzles

Using mental math to add helps you find tens and hundreds.

1. Find two numbers in the box whose sum equals each number in the puzzle board. Use each number *only once*. Do not use paper and pencil or a calculator.

119	225	511	259	173	28
486	374	375	227	164	314
389	136	72	241	81	326

Puzzle Board		
100 ____ + ____	200 ____ + ____	300 ____ + ____
400 ____ + ____	500 ____ + ____	600 ____ + ____
700 ____ + ____	800 ____ + ____	900 ____ + ____

2. Explain what methods you used to solve.

____

____

Name ______________________________

Daily Review
2-2

1. Which is seven hundred eighty thousand, two hundred sixteen written using base-ten numerals?

Ⓐ 780,216
Ⓑ 708,216
Ⓒ 78,261
Ⓓ 78,216

2. The fourth-grade class sold 1,125 raffle tickets. The fifth-grade class sold 1,075 raffle tickets. How many raffle tickets did the classes sell in all? Use mental math to solve.

Ⓐ 1,200 raffle tickets
Ⓑ 2,000 raffle tickets
Ⓒ 2,100 raffle tickets
Ⓓ 2,200 raffle tickets

3. Which time is shown on the clock?

Ⓐ 4:52 Ⓒ 3:52
Ⓑ 4:12 Ⓓ 3:12

4. What is 21,883 rounded to the nearest hundred?

Ⓐ 21,900
Ⓑ 21,800
Ⓒ 21,000
Ⓓ 20,000

5. Write 3,492 in expanded form.

____

6. Write thirty-four thousand, two hundred sixty-six using base-ten numerals.

____

7. On Thursday, 13,450 people attended a baseball game. Only 11,350 people attended the game on Friday. How many more people attended the game on Thursday than the game on Friday? Explain how to use mental math to solve.

____

____

____

____

____

____

8. How many times greater is the first 5 than the second 5 in 853,539?

____

Name ______________________________

Reteach to Build Understanding
2-2

Vocabulary

An **estimate** is an approximate number or answer. One way to estimate sums and differences is to **round** before adding or subtracting.

1. Round 54,792 to the nearest thousand.

What digit is in thousands place? ______

2. To round, look at the digit to the right of the rounding place.

What is the digit to the right of thousands in 54,792? ______

If the digit is 5 or greater, add 1 to the digit in the rounding place. If the digit is less than 5, leave the digit in the rounding place alone.

All the digits to the right of the rounding place become zeros.

3. What is 54,792 to the nearest thousand? ______________

4. Round each addend to the nearest ten thousand, and then estimate the sum.

337,961 + 432,746

______________ + ______________ = ______________

5. Estimate the sum.

97,991 + 102,489

______________ + ______________ = ______________

6. Estimate the difference.

645,908 − 335,297

______________ − ______________ = ______________

On the Back!

7. Write an equation using two addends that, when rounded to the nearest thousand, result in a sum of 47,000. Explain how you chose the addends.

Name ______________________________

Build Mathematical Literacy
2-2

Read the problem. Answer the questions to help understand the problem.

A football team needs to sell at least 20,000 tickets to two games to cover expenses. They sell 10,184 tickets to one game and 9,723 to the other. Estimate by rounding to the nearest thousand and by rounding to the nearest hundred. Did the team sell enough tickets? Explain your answer.

1. The first sentence tells the main idea of the problem. What is that main idea?

2. Which math operation will you need to use to solve this problem?

3. What important information is found in the second sentence?

4. Will you use the numbers found in the second sentence, exactly as they are?

5. What is the next step after you round the numbers?

6. After you find the sum of the estimated numbers, what should you do?

7. Why do you think the problem asks you to round to the nearest thousand and to the nearest hundred?

Name ___________________________

Enrichment
2-2

Family Vacation

The Bravo family is planning a family vacation.

- They plan to drive from Miami to New York City.
- They want to stop and spend some time in Washington, D.C.
- Mr. Bravo thinks they can average driving 60 miles an hour.

Distance between Cities

Cities	Miles
Miami to Washington, D.C.	1,043 miles
Washington, D.C., to New York City	237 miles

1. The family starts their trip on Monday morning at 9 A.M. They stop at noon for lunch. How many miles have they traveled?

____

2. Estimate how far the Bravo family is from Washington, D.C., at noon.

____

3. After their one-hour lunch, the Bravo family continues driving. At 7 P.M. they stop for dinner and check into a hotel. How far did the family travel after lunch? How far did the family drive on the first day of their trip?

____

4. On the second day, the Bravo family begins driving at 7 A.M. That day, they stop for a total of 2 hours. Will they get to Washington, D.C., by 5 P.M.? Explain.

____

____

5. Estimate the total distance the Bravo family must drive from Miami to New York City and back. Explain.

____

____

____

Name ______________________________

1. Florida has a total area of 65,758 square miles. It has a land area of 53,997 square miles. The rest is water area. Which is the best estimate of the water area?

Ⓐ About 10,000 square miles
Ⓑ About 12,000 square miles
Ⓒ About 18,000 square miles
Ⓓ About 30,000 square miles

2. Which statement best compares the values of the fours in 144,202?

Ⓐ The value of the 4 in the ten thousands place is one hundred times as great as the value of the 4 in the thousands place.
Ⓑ The value of the 4 in the ten thousands place is ten times as great as the value of the 4 in the thousands place.
Ⓒ The value of the 4 in the thousands place is ten times as great as the value of the 4 in the ten thousands place.
Ⓓ The value of the 4 in the thousands place is one hundred times as great as the value of the 4 in the ten thousands place.

3. A newspaper sold 441,902 copies last week. The editor wants to round that number to the nearest ten thousand for a report. Which number should he use in the report?

Ⓐ 400,000
Ⓑ 440,000
Ⓒ 441,900
Ⓓ 442,000

Use the table below for Exercises **4–7**.

Volunteers took an online survey about their favorite animal.

Animals	Votes
Lion	1,216
Tiger	2,378
Monkey	1,192
Bear	1,139

4. Rounded to the nearest hundred, how many people voted for bears?

____

5. About how many people voted for lions and tigers? Explain how you estimated the sum.

____

____

____

6. How many more people voted for monkeys than for bears? Use mental math to solve.

____

7. Write the number of people that voted for lions in expanded form and using number names.

____

____

____

Name ______________________________

Vocabulary

1. A **sum** is the answer to an addition problem.
Addends are the numbers you add to find the sum.

?		
84	176	159

The addends in this bar diagram are _______, _______, and _______.

2. Find 84 + 176 + 159.

Step 1: Line up the ones, tens, and hundreds.

$$\begin{array}{r} 84 \\ 176 \\ +\,159 \\ \hline \end{array}$$

Step 2: Add the ones. Regroup if needed.

4 + 6 + 9 = _______ ones

Regroup _______ ones as _______ ten and _______ ones.

$$\begin{array}{r} \square \\ 84 \\ 176 \\ +\,159 \\ \hline \square \end{array}$$

Step 3: Add the tens. Regroup if needed.

1 ten + 8 tens + _______ tens + _______ tens = _______ tens

Regroup _______ tens as _______ hundreds and _______ ten.

$$\begin{array}{r} \square\,1 \\ 84 \\ 176 \\ +\,159 \\ \hline \square 9 \end{array}$$

Step 4: Add the hundreds.

_______ hundreds + 1 hundred + 1 hundred = _______ hundreds

So, 84 + 176 + 159 = _______.

$$\begin{array}{r} 2\,1 \\ 84 \\ 176 \\ +\,159 \\ \hline \square 19 \end{array}$$

3. Another way to add three numbers is to add two numbers first.
Then, add the sum of those two numbers and the third number.

Find 407 + 189 + 220.

Step 1: $\begin{array}{r} 407 \\ +\,189 \\ \hline \end{array}$ **Step 2:** $\begin{array}{r} 596 \\ +\,220 \\ \hline \end{array}$

So, 407 + 189 + 220 = _______.

On the Back!

4. Find 216 + 134 + 168. Show two different ways to find the sum.

Name ____________________

Build Mathematical Literacy
2-3

Read and answer the questions to learn how to solve the problem.

A Miami Little League team played a doubleheader (two back-to-back baseball games). The first game lasted 155 minutes. The second game lasted 175 minutes. There was a 30-minute break between games. What was the total time of the doubleheader?

1. Can the problem be answered in one step?

 ____

2. What information in the problem do you need to use to solve the problem?

 ____

 ____

3. Is there any extra information given in the problem?

 ____

4. What label will your answer have? Is there another answer and label that your answer could have?

 ____

 ____

5. Underline the numbers you will use.

6. What operation will you use to solve this problem? Explain.

 ____

 ____

7. Show your calculations. What would your answer be in hours and minutes?

 ____

 ____

Name

Slippery Digits

For each exercise, follow the directions to form an addition problem and find its sum. There may be more than one solution.

1. Use each of the digits 5, 6, 7, and 9 once. Fill in the boxes to make a sum greater than 130.

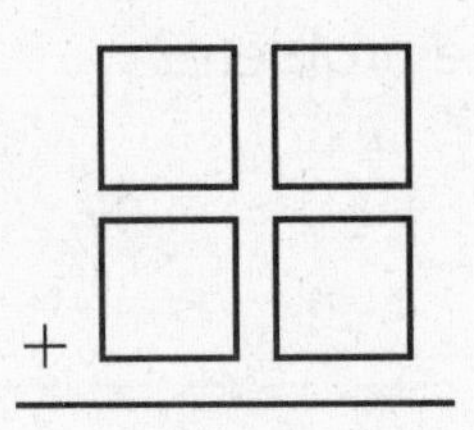

2. Use each of the digits 3, 4, 5, and 6 once. Fill in the boxes to make a sum greater than 100.

3. Make a sum greater than 1,000. Use any digits, but do not use a digit more than twice.

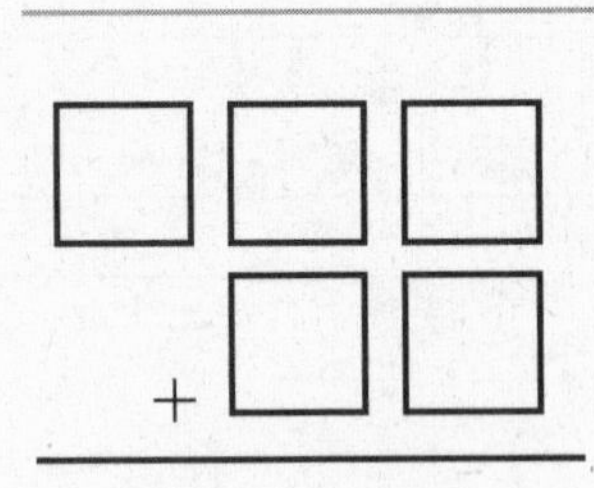

4. Use 6 different digits. Fill in the boxes to make the largest sum possible.

5. Use 4 different digits. Fill in the boxes to make the smallest 2-digit sum possible.

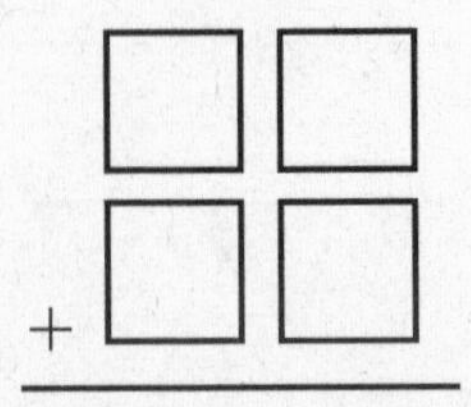

6. Use 6 different digits. Fill in the boxes to make the smallest 3-digit sum possible.

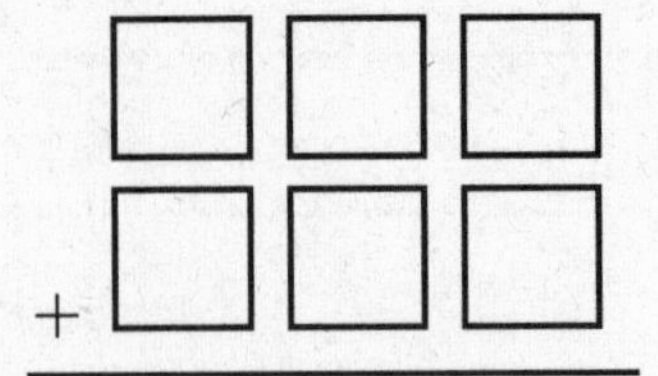

Name ___________________________

Daily Review
2-4

1. Which statement best describes the value of each seven in 7,170?

Ⓐ The value of the 7 in the thousands place is 10 times as great as the 7 in the tens place.

Ⓑ The value of 7 in the thousands place is 2 times as great as the 7 in the tens place.

Ⓒ The value of the 7 in the thousands place is 100 times as great as the 7 in the tens place.

Ⓓ The value of 7 in the tens place is 100 times as great as the value of the 7 in the thousands place.

2. Select all correct addition equations.

- ☐ $79 + 140 = 119$
- ☐ $452 + 157 = 609$
- ☐ $362 + 73 = 435$
- ☐ $51 + 83 = 134$
- ☐ $243 + 683 = 926$

3. Which number is forty thousand, twenty-six?

Ⓐ 4,026

Ⓑ 426

Ⓒ 42,600

Ⓓ 40,026

4. Find the sum.

$$\begin{array}{r} 463 \\ +\,808 \\ \hline \end{array}$$

5. Find the sum.

$$\begin{array}{r} 72 \\ 37 \\ 28 \\ +\,65 \\ \hline \end{array}$$

6. Last season, a tree farm sold 148 oak trees, 259 maple trees, and 175 pine trees. How many trees were sold?

____

7. Write three numbers that round to 32,000 when rounded to the nearest thousand.

____

____

8. Write the number for five hundred fifty six thousand, two hundred ninety-seven.

____

9. Round 142,895 to the nearest ten thousand.

____

Name ______________________________

Vocabulary

1. An **algorithm** is a set of steps used to solve a problem. The standard algorithm for adding whole numbers is shown.

Use the steps to find the sum.

$$\begin{array}{r} 34,227 \\ +\ 12,321 \\ \hline \square\square,\square\square\square \end{array}$$

1. Add the ones. Regroup if needed.
2. Add the tens. Regroup if needed.
3. Add the hundreds. Regroup if needed.
4. Add the thousands. Regroup if needed.
5. Add the ten thousands. Regroup if needed.

2. Find 2,835 + 429.

Write the addends. Align place values. Then use the algorithm to add.

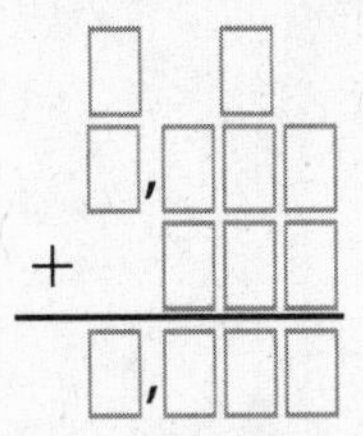

5 + 9 = 14
Regroup: 14 = 1 ten + 4 ones

3. Estimate to check if your answer to Exercise 2 is reasonable. Explain.

____

____

4. Add 62,810 + 89,467.

Write the addends. Align place values. Then use the algorithm to add.

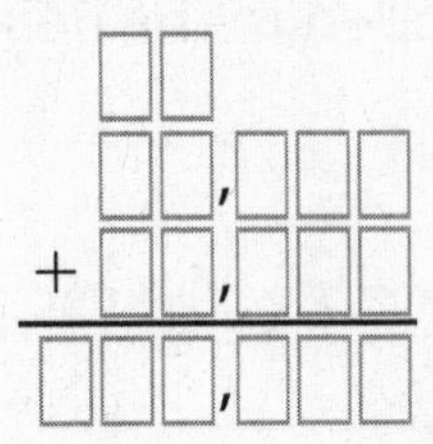

5. Estimate to check if your answer to Exercise 4 is reasonable. Explain.

____

____

____

On the Back!

6. Find 1,567 + 302 + 984. Estimate to check.

Name ______________________

Build Mathematical Literacy
2-4

Read the problem. Then, break down the main problem into smaller problems.

Higher Order Thinking Explain the mistake made when finding the sum at the right. What is the correct sum?

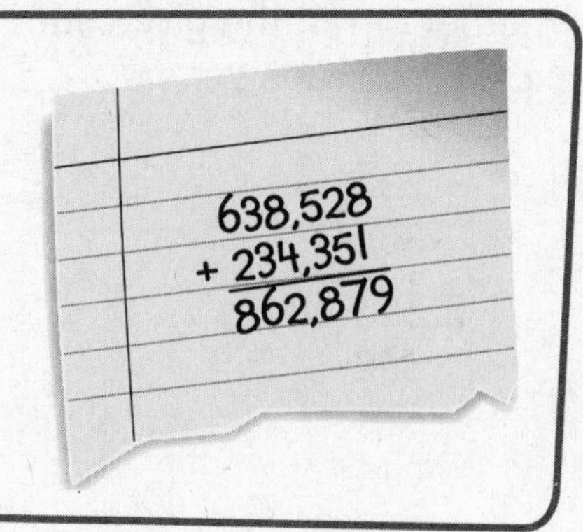

1. How could you check for a mistake in a problem?

____

____

2. When adding two greater numbers, what is a mistake that could be made?

____

____

Name ________________________________

Enrichment
2-4

Use Your Head

Look at each problem and its sum. Without actually adding, decide whether or not the given sum is reasonable. Write ***Yes*** or ***No***, and explain your answer.

1.
```
  224
  303
+ 125
-----
  652
```
____

____

____

2.
```
  300
  478
+ 213
-----
  991
```
____

____

____

3.
```
  324
  156
+ 615
-----
  100
```
____

____

____

4.
```
   18,207
    4,956
+   2,345
---------
  101,217
```
____

____

____

5.
```
  131,058
   20,790
+  18,903
---------
  170,751
```
____

____

____

6.
```
  202,341
  137,750
+ 145,532
---------
   80,623
```
____

____

____

Name ______________________

Daily Review

2-5

1. Paula's family sells lemonade at county fairs during the summer. The table below shows the number of cups of lemonade they sold each month.

Lemonade Sales

Month	Number of Cups Sold
May	410
June	1,438
July	4,899
August	2,145

What was the total number of cups Paula's family sold?

Ⓐ 8,453 cups

Ⓑ 8,763 cups

Ⓒ 8,882 cups

Ⓓ 8,892 cups

2. What is 12,389 rounded to the nearest hundred?

Ⓐ 12,000

Ⓑ 12,300

Ⓒ 12,390

Ⓓ 12,400

3. Estimate the difference by rounding to the nearest thousand.

35,792 − 24,702

Ⓐ About 12,000

Ⓑ About 11,000

Ⓒ About 10,000

Ⓓ About 9,000

4. A surveyor records the number of cars in a shopping center parking lot for three days. 1,398 cars parked in the lot the first day, 2,723 cars parked in the lot the second day, and 1,384 cars parked in the lot the third day. How many cars parked in the lot all three days?

____

5. Explain how to use mental math to add 1,037 + 1,033.

____

____

____

____

6. Compare. Write >, =, or <.

34,929 ◯ 34,919

7. Write 249,958 in expanded form.

____

____

8. Write 408,629 in word form.

____

____

____

Name ______________________________

Vocabulary

1. To **regroup** is to name a whole number in a different way.

Sometimes the number from which you are subtracting will have 1 zero.
Regroup 1 hundred as 10 tens to write 403 in a different way.

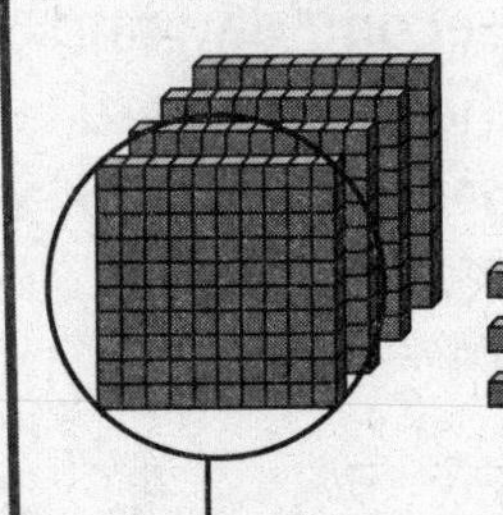

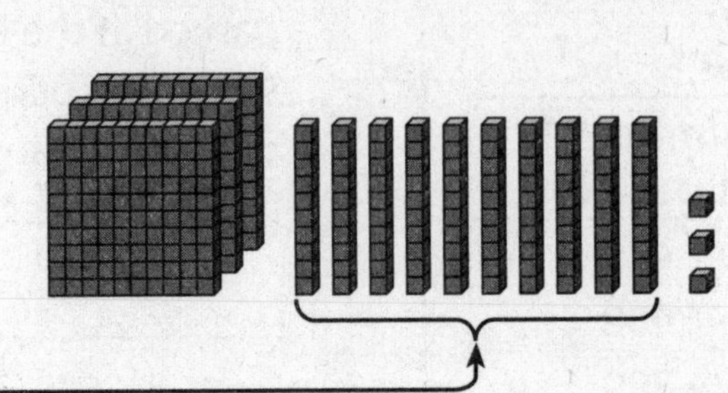

4 hundreds and 3 ones can be regrouped as

_______ hundreds,

_______ tens, and

_______ ones.

2. Sometimes the number you are subtracting from will have 2 zeros.
Regroup 1 hundred as 9 tens and 10 ones to write 400 in a different way.

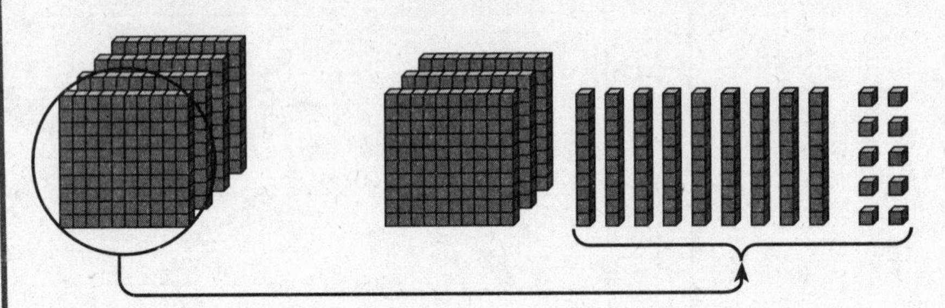

4 hundreds can be regrouped as

_______ hundreds,

_______ tens, and

_______ ones.

3. Find 502 − 215.

Step 1: Subtract the ones.
2 ones < 5 ones
Since there are no tens in 502, regroup hundreds into tens.

5 hundreds and 0 tens = 4 hundreds and _______ tens

Step 2: Regroup tens into ones.
10 tens and 2 ones = _______ tens and _______ ones

Step 3: Subtract the ones, the tens, and then the hundreds.

So, 502 − 215 = _______.

☐	☐	
5̸	0̸	2
− 2	1	5

	☐	☐
4	10	
5̸	0̸	2̸
− 2	1	5

	9	
4	10	12
5̸	0̸	2̸
− 2	1	5
☐	☐	☐

On the Back!

4. Find 300 − 178. Then use addition to check your answer, or use estimation to see if your answer is reasonable.

Name ______________________________

Read the problem below. Select the answer to each question.

Higher Order Thinking What mistake did Leon make? What is the correct difference?

Leon

```
 6 18 13
 7 9 3
-5 7 6
------
 1 1 7
```

1. Which expression represents the ones in this problem?

   Ⓐ $6 - 3$
   Ⓑ $3 + 6$
   Ⓒ $13 - 6$
   Ⓓ $13 + 6$

2. What does the number 18 represent in the problem?

   Ⓐ The number of tens from which 7 is subtracted
   Ⓑ The number of ones from which 7 is subtracted
   Ⓒ The number of tens that are subtracted from 793
   Ⓓ The number of ones that are subtracted from 793

3. Which operation do you use to find 1 in the tens place of 117?

   Ⓐ Addition
   Ⓑ Subtraction
   Ⓒ Multiplication
   Ⓓ Division

4. What was Leon's error? Explain.

____

____

____

____

____

____

Name ______________________________

Cross Number Puzzle

Find the sums and differences to complete the cross number puzzle.

Across

1. 790 − 178
3. 199 + 123
4. 172 + 374
5. 9756 − 5336
7. 4289 − 1173
9. 1100 − 890
10. 621 − 348

Down

1. 1185 + 5367
2. 448 − 224
3. 512 − 120
4. 1009 − 458
6. 630 − 198
7. 173 + 179
8. 621 − 478

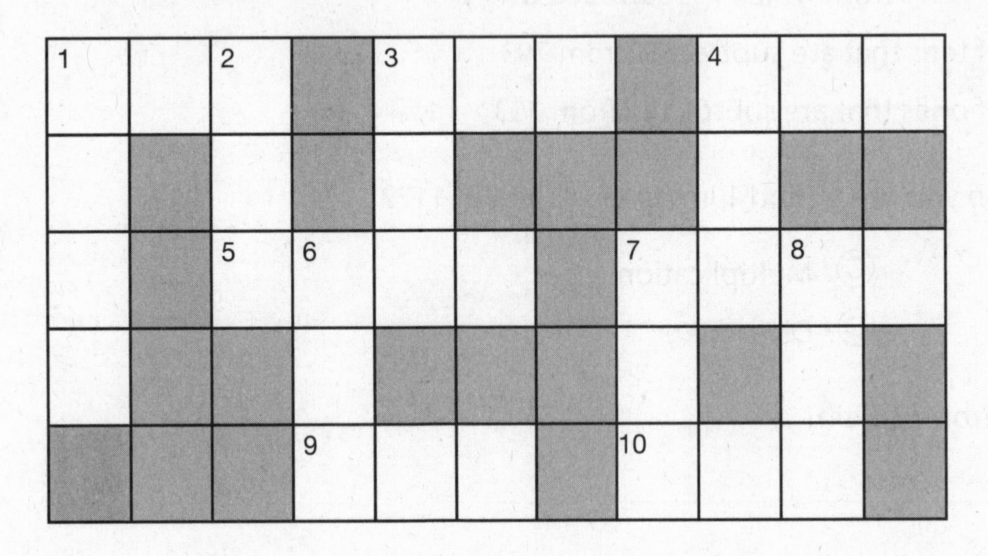

Name ______________________

Daily Review

2-6

1. Select all true comparisons.

- ☐ $870,496 < 87,518$
- ☐ $69,245 > 69,218$
- ☐ $208,035 < 280,350$
- ☐ $766,455 > 776,352$
- ☐ $398,054 < 398,045$

2. When rounded to the nearest hundred, select all the numbers that will have a 9 in the hundreds place.

- ☐ 398,942
- ☐ 72,985
- ☐ 64,812
- ☐ 128,874
- ☐ 140,939

3. A market sold 652 bags of apples in August, 748 bags in September, and 814 bags in October. About how many bags of apples did the market sell in those three months?

Ⓐ 2,100 bags

Ⓑ 220 bags

Ⓒ 2,200 bags

Ⓓ 2,300 bags

4. Find the sum.

$575 + 294$

Ⓐ 829

Ⓑ 869

Ⓒ 896

Ⓓ 986

5. Explain how to estimate the sum of $378,903 + 613,964$.

6. What are two ways to write 37,614 in expanded form?

7. Which number is greater 101,901 or 101,099?

8. Describe when you need to break apart a hundred for a subtraction problem, and describe what you do.

Name ______________________

Reteach to Build Understanding
2-6

Vocabulary

1. The **standard subtraction algorithm** is shown.

```
    8 10 13
 57,9 1 3
-20,4 6 8
 □□□□□
```

1. Regroup 1 ten 3 ones = 0 tens 13 ones. Then subtract the ones.
2. Regroup and subtract tens.
3. Regroup and subtract hundreds.
4. Subtract thousands.
5. Subtract ten thousands.

2. Write 82,571 − 59,347 aligning the digits by place value. Then use the standard algorithm to subtract.

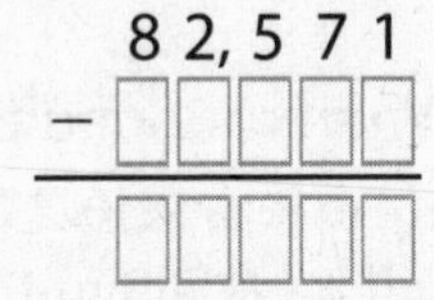

3. Estimate the difference in Exercise 2.

80,000 − __________ = __________

4. Is your answer to Exercise 2 reasonable? Explain.

____

____

5. Estimate 76,397 − 27,999.

____

6. Use the standard algorithm to subtract. Use your estimate to check that your answer is reasonable.

```
  76,397
 −27,999
 □□□□□
```

On the Back!

7. Find 795,362 − 469,989. Explain how to check that your answer is reasonable.

Name ______________________

Build Mathematical Literacy
2-6

Read the text and look at the chart. Then, use both to answer the questions.

How many more people attended the street fair in 2019 than in 2017 and 2018 combined?

DATA

Attendance at Street Fair	
2017	81,129
2018	112,172
2019	362,839

1. What does the chart show?

____

____

2. How was 2019 different from the other years?

____

____

3. What does the question ask you to find?

____

____

4. What does the word "combined" tell you in the problem?

____

5. What does the phrase "how many more" tell you?

____

____

6. How can you use estimation to make sure your answer is reasonable?

____

____

____

____

Name ______________________

Enrichment
2-6

What's Missing?

Solve for the missing values.

1. 35,617 − ◯ = 15,624　　　　◯ = ______

2. 196,783 − 89,564 = □　　　　□ = ______

3. △ − 42,876 = 33,418　　　　△ = ______

4. 252,891 − ● = 107,000　　　　● = ______

5. ■ − 7,392 = 12,183　　　　■ = ______

6. 94,784 − 33,587 = ▲　　　　▲ = ______

Use the values to subtract.

7. ● − △ = ______

8. ▲ − ■ − ◯ = ______

9. ● − □ = ______

10. ◯ − ■ = ______

Name ____________________

Daily Review

2-7

1. Which number is thirty-two thousand, four hundred eight written with base-ten numerals?

Ⓐ 32,480
Ⓑ 32,408
Ⓒ 30,248
Ⓓ 30,240

2. The Canines sold 4,038 tickets to their soccer game. The Felines sold 6,224 tickets to their game. How many more tickets did the Felines sell than the Canines?

Ⓐ 2,186 tickets
Ⓑ 2,196 tickets
Ⓒ 2,286 tickets
Ⓓ 10,262 tickets

3. Alvin rounded 336,457 to 340,000. To what place did Alvin round the number?

Ⓐ Tens
Ⓑ Hundreds
Ⓒ Thousands
Ⓓ Ten thousands

4. Which sum or difference is equal to 12,492? Select all that apply.

☐ 8,572 + 3,920
☐ 7,279 + 5,203
☐ 4,100 + 8,392
☐ 15,728 − 3,246
☐ 19,412 − 6,920

5. Norman answered the question below.

Lilith walked 15,258 steps on Monday and 12,474 steps on Tuesday. How many more steps did Lilith walk on Monday than Tuesday?

Lilith walked 2,784 more steps on Monday than Tuesday.

Is Norman's answer reasonable? Explain.

____
____
____
____
____
____

6. What is 195,243 − 75,489?

____

7. Bill bought 3 packs of 4 hamburgers, 2 packs of 6 turkey burgers, and 1 pack of 8 veggie burgers for the picnic. How many burgers did Bill buy?

____
____

Name ______________________________

Reteach to Build Understanding
2-7

Vocabulary

1. **Regrouping** is used to name a whole number in a different way. Regroup to complete each statement.

   1 ten = ______ ones

   1 hundred = ______ tens

   2 tens, 2 ones = 1 ten, ______ ones

   3 hundreds, 6 tens = 2 hundreds, ______ tens.

2. Subtract 30,220 − 4,116.

   Write the problem vertically, and use the algorithm to find the difference.

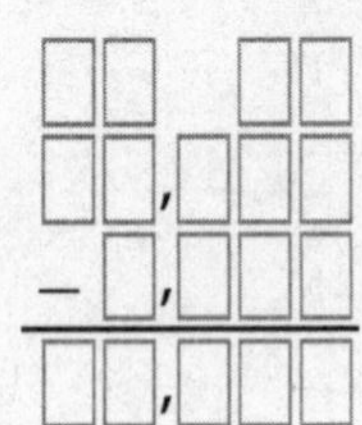

1. Subtract the ones. Regroup.

   2 tens = 1 ten, ______ ones
2. Subtract the tens.
3. Subtract the hundreds.
4. Subtract the thousands. Regroup.

   3 ten thousands = ______ ten thousands, 10 thousands

3. Subtract 830,502 − 746,319.

   Write the problem vertically, and use the algorithm to find the difference.

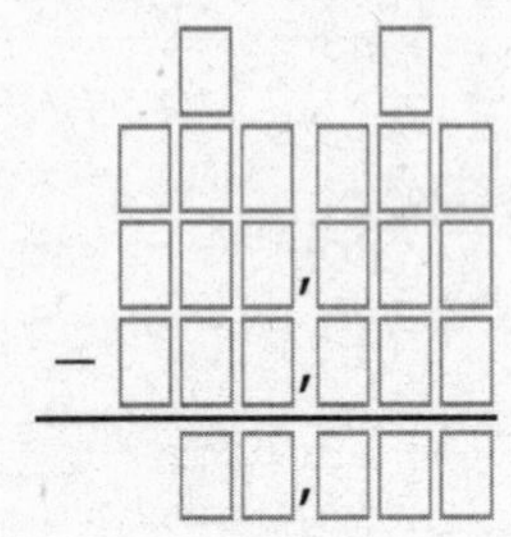

On the Back!

4. Subtract 78,305 − 56,419. Explain how to use estimation to check that your answer is reasonable.

Name ______________________________

Build Mathematical Literacy
2-7

Read the problem. Then, answer the questions to help you better understand the problem.

Will the difference between 44,041 and 43,876 be greater or less than 1,000? Explain.

1. Underline the word "difference." What clue does this word give you?

____

2. Underline the words "greater or less than." What clue do these words give you?

____

____

____

____

3. How could you use addition to solve this problem?

____

____

4. Is adding or subtracting an easier way to solve the problem?

____

____

5. Why can addition be used even though it says "difference" in the problem?

____

____

____

____

____

Name ___________________________________

Enrichment
2-7

Transportation Conclusions

Each person made a conclusion about the data in the table. Think about each person's conclusion. Do you agree? Explain.

Airports and Railways

Country	Number of Airports	Length of Railways (km)
Australia	455	47,738
Finland	148	5,741
France	501	29,085
Germany	554	47,201
Hungary	46	7,937
Japan	175	23,556
New Zealand	118	4,128

1. Kylie compared the length of railways in Australia and Japan. She concluded that Australia has 24,282 kilometers more railway than Japan.

____

____

2. Franklin looked at the number of airports in Germany and Hungary. He concluded that Germany has 508 more airports than Hungary.

____

____

3. Theona concluded that France has 11,279 more kilometers of railway than Hungary, New Zealand, and Finland altogether.

____

____

Name ______________________________

Daily Review
2-8

1. A florist delivered 1,024 flowers during the month of May and 548 flowers during the month of June. How many flowers did the florist deliver during the two months?

Ⓐ 1,572 flowers
Ⓑ 1,570 flowers
Ⓒ 1,562 flowers
Ⓓ 1,524 flowers

2. Which is the difference of 45,026 − 13,492?

Ⓐ 31,534
Ⓑ 31,543
Ⓒ 32,534
Ⓓ 32,543

3. For which number is the value of the digit in the hundred thousands place ten times as great as the value of the digit in the ten thousands place?

Ⓐ 242,455
Ⓑ 224,455
Ⓒ 212,553
Ⓓ 202,222

4. Bay City has a population of 49,542. What is Bay City's population rounded to the nearest thousand?

Ⓐ 49,000
Ⓑ 49,542
Ⓒ 50,000
Ⓓ 60,000

5. During a book drive, one charity group donated 3,402 books. Another charity group donated 3,420 books. Complete the comparison. Write >, = , or <.

3,402 ◯ 3,420

6. At its farthest point, the moon is 252,088 miles away from Earth. Jillene said the moon is about 250,000 miles away from Earth. To what place did Jillene round the distance?

____

7. A local library has two floors. The library has a total of 15,293 books. There are 5,392 books on the first floor. How many books are on the second floor? Explain how you know your answer is reasonable.

____

____

____

____

____

____

8. Write eighty-six thousand, two hundred eleven using base-ten numerals.

____

Name ______________________________

Reteach to Build Understanding
2-8

Vocabulary

1. An **equation** is a number sentence that uses the equal sign (=) to show that two expressions have the same value.

   Write an equation to show 32,947 + 17,374 and the sum.

   __________ + __________ = __________

2. A **variable** is a symbol or letter that stands for a number. Identify the variable in the equation $102,832 + p = 270,013$.

   ____

Use Exercises 3–5 to answer the question.

Gary and Leona traveled a total of 72,648 miles last year on business. Gary traveled 43,975 miles. How many miles did Leona travel?

3. What quantities are given in the problem, and what do the numbers mean?

   ____

   ____

4. Complete the bar diagram to show how to find, *t*, the number of miles Leona traveled.

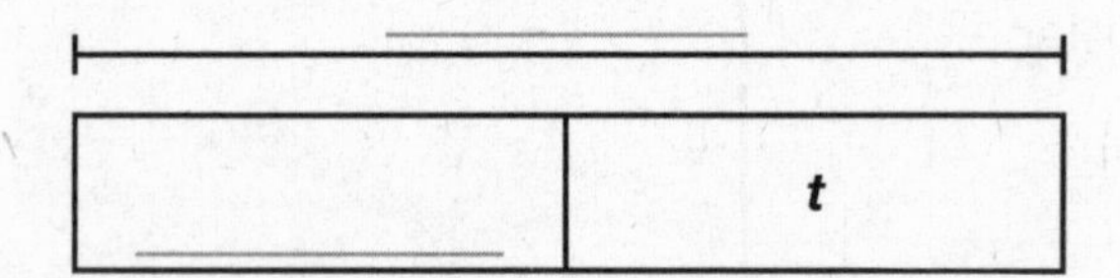

5. Write and solve an equation to answer the question.

   ____

On the Back!

6. Wyoming has a land area of 93,140 square miles. Oregon has a land area 2,856 square miles greater than Wyoming. What is the land area of Oregon? Draw a bar diagram, and write and solve an equation for the bar diagram.

Name ______________________

Build Mathematical Literacy
2-8

Read the problem. Then, complete the tasks below.

A wall is being built from 16,351 stones. The builders have placed 8,361 stones, and they have 7,944 stones left. Do they have enough stones? How many more stones do they need?
What quantities are given in the problem, and what do the numbers mean?

1. What does the number 16,351 represent? Sketch a picture of a simple wall, and label the sketch with 16,351 stones.

2. What does the number 8,361 represent?

3. What does the number 7,944 represent in the problem?

4. What is the problem asking you to do?

5. What operation will you use to find the total number of stones the builders have?

6. How do you determine how many more stones the builders need?

Name ______________________

Flying High

	Atlanta	Boston	Chicago	Dallas	Denver
Boston	946				
Chicago	606	867			
Dallas	721	1,555	796		
Denver	1,208	1,767	901	654	
Detroit	505	632	235	982	1,135

Use the air distance chart above to write equations for each problem. Then solve.

1. How many more miles does it take to get from Denver to Atlanta through Chicago than through Dallas?

____

____

____

____

2. How many more miles is it to fly round trip between Dallas and Boston than between Dallas and Detroit?

____

____

____

____

3. Jorge lives in Denver. One grandmother lives in Chicago and the other lives in Boston. How many miles can he save by visiting the grandmother in Chicago and then the grandmother in Boston before returning home rather than making a round trip from home to each?

____

Name ___________________________

Home-School Connection

Topic **3**

Use Strategies and Properties to Multiply by 1-Digit Numbers

Dear Family,

Your child is learning strategies to multiply two-, three-, and four-digit numbers by one-digit numbers. He or she is applying strategies involving partial products, including place-value and area models.

These patterns also help your child estimate products. For example, to estimate 4×32, round 32 to the nearest ten (30) and then multiply ($4 \times 30 = 120$). To find the actual product, your child can use the Distributive Property.

Break apart 32 into 30 and 2. Think of 4×32 as $(4 \times 30) + (4 \times 2)$. So, $120 + 8 = 128$.

Your child can compare the product to the estimate to see if his or her answer is reasonable.

Multiplying Greater Numbers

Materials paper and pencil

Give your child a two-digit by one-digit multiplication problem, such as 5×49. Ask your child to estimate the product and then solve. He or she can use the Distributive Property to find the product.

Observe Your Child

Ask your child if his or her answer is reasonable when solving a problem multiplying a one-digit number by a two-, three-, or four-digit number. Then have your child explain his or her reasoning.

Nombre ______________________________

De la escuela al hogar
(en español)
Tema 3

Usar estrategias y propiedades para multiplicar por números de 1 dígito

Estimada familia:

Su niño(a) está aprendiendo estrategias para multiplicar números de dos, tres y cuatro dígitos por números de un dígito. Él o ella está usando estrategias que se tratan de productos parciales, incluyendo modelos de valor de posición y modelos de área.

Estos patrones también ayudan a su niño(a) a estimar productos. Por ejemplo, para estimar 4×32, se redondea 32 a la decena más cercana (30) y, luego, se multiplica ($4 \times 30 = 120$). Para hallar el producto real, su niño(a) puede usar la propiedad distributiva.

Se descompone 32 en 30 y 2. Se piensa en 4×32 como $(4 \times 30) + (4 \times 2)$. Por tanto, $120 + 8 = 128$.

Su niño(a) puede comparar el producto con la estimación para ver si su respuesta es razonable.

Multiplicar números más grandes

Materiales papel y lápiz

Muéstrele a su niño(a) una multiplicación de un número de dos dígitos por un número de un dígito, como 5×49. Pídale que estime el producto y, luego, resuelva la multiplicación. Su niño(a) puede usar la propiedad distributiva para hallar el producto.

Observe a su niño(a)

Pregúntele si su respuesta es razonable cuando resuelve problemas multiplicando un número de un dígito por un número de dos, tres o cuatro dígitos. Luego, pídale que explique su razonamiento.

Name ___________________________

Pick a Project

Project 3A

Key Lime Pie

Key lime pie is made with Key limes from the Florida Keys. Key limes are different from Persian limes, which are the kinds of limes you usually see in a market. The rind (or outer covering) and the juice of a Key lime are more yellow than the green rind and juice of Persian limes. Key lime pie is the official pie of the state of Florida.

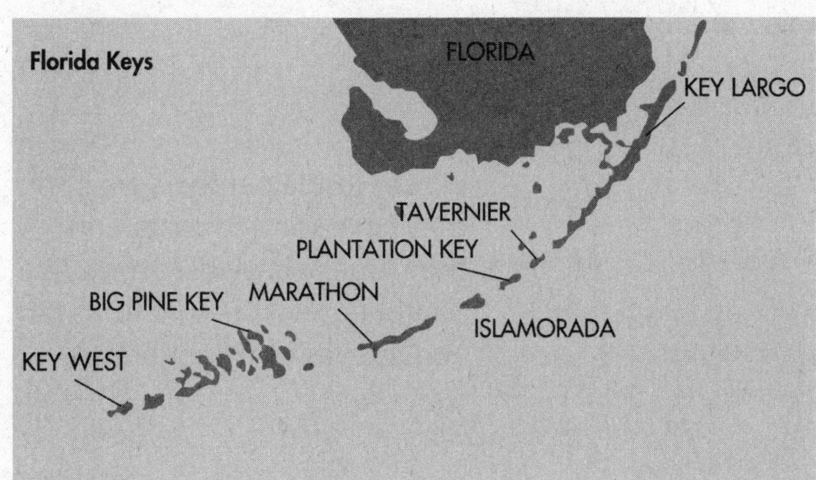

Key lime pie is also made with condensed milk, which is a canned milk that does not require refrigeration. When Key lime pie was first developed, it was important to use condensed milk since refrigerators were not widely available, especially out in the Florida Keys.

Your Project Create Data for the Amount of an Ingredient for Key Lime Pie

Research some Key lime pie recipes. How much lime zest is used when making a Key lime pie? The zest of a lime is the outer layer of the lime's rind. Imagine that you own a large bakery. How many teaspoons of lime zest would you need to make 50, 500, and 5,000 Key lime pies? Choose another ingredient and determine how much of that ingredient you would need to make 80, 800, and 8,000 Key lime pies.

Create a presentation that shows how many teaspoons of lime zest you need for each number of pies and how you found your values. Do the same for the other ingredient you chose. Present your strategies and your work to the class.

Name ____________________

Pick a Project

Project 3B

Florida Panther

In 1982, the Florida panther was named the official animal of the state of Florida. The Florida panther is a kind of mountain lion that lives mostly in the forests of southern Florida. Currently, the Florida panther is on a list of endangered species, which means that there are very few of them. As of 2017, it is estimated that there are only 120 to 230 Florida panthers.

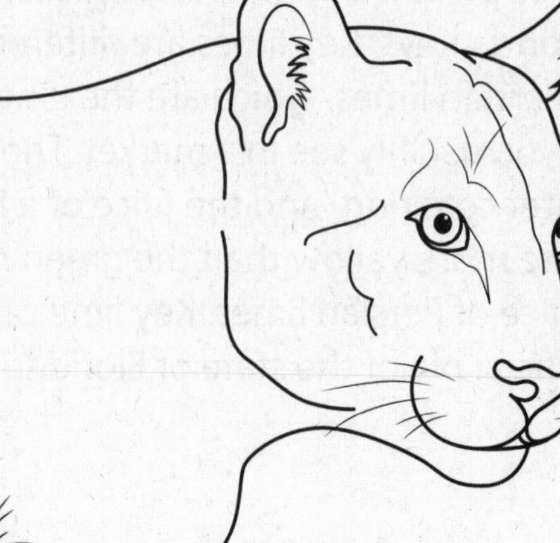

When Florida panthers are born, they have spotted coats, and they usually have blue eyes. As a panther grows, its coat turns tan and its eyes turn light brown.

Your Project Find the Weight of Florida Panthers

Female Florida panthers weigh about 70–75 pounds. Suppose that a Big Cat Preserve needs to rescue 12 female Florida panthers from a tourist attraction that is closing. Estimate the total weight of the 12 panthers. What is the most the panthers could weigh? Compare your estimate to the product.

Draw a picture of a Florida panther, and write a caption that tells how you estimated and then calculated the total weight of the panthers. Share your strategies and your work with another student.

Name ___________________________

Pick a Project

Project 3C

Giraffes

Giraffes are mammals that are native to Africa. They are the tallest living land animal with heights of up to 20 feet. A giraffe's diet consists mostly of the leaves, fruits, and flowers of plants and trees. At the end of 2016, the giraffe was identified as being vulnerable to extinction. It is estimated that fewer than 100,000 giraffes currently live in the wild.

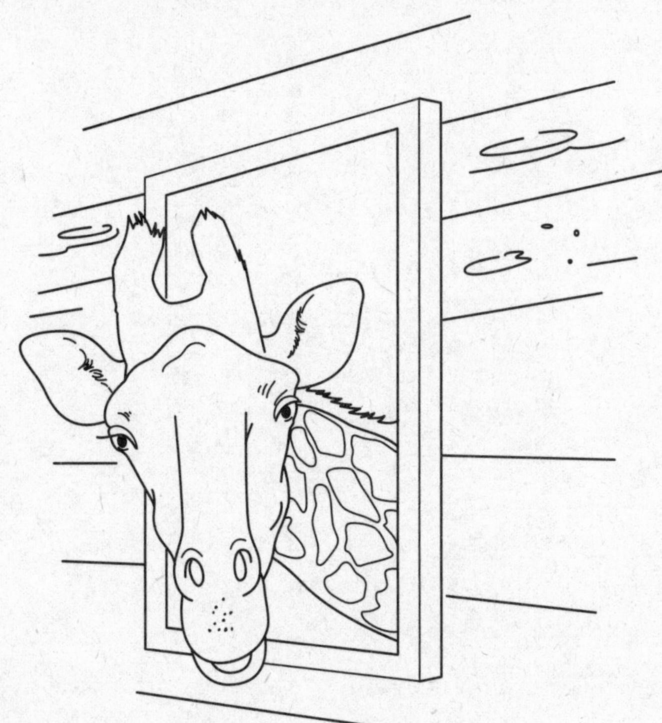

Giraffes are known mostly for their very long necks and legs, as well as their unique coats. Giraffes tend to live in herds.

Your Project Find the Mass of Giraffes

An average male giraffe has a mass of about 1,192 kilograms. Imagine that you are looking at 3 male giraffes. What is their total mass? Use arrays and partial products to find the answer.

Create a song describing the array you created, the partial products you found, and the total mass of the 3 giraffes. Record your song and plan its release to your class, including cover art.

Name ______________________________

Measurements on Maps

Did You Know? You can use a scale factor to find distances between cities on a map. The scale factor is a number that relates the size of the map to the size of the actual land.

Cities	Estimated Distance
New York, NY to Los Angeles, CA	6 paper clips
Phoenix, AZ to Philadelphia, PA	5 paper clips
Seattle, WA to Wichita, KS	4 paper clips
Miami, FL to Detroit, MI	3 paper clips
Boise, ID to Phoenix, AZ	2 paper clips

The table at the right shows the estimated distances between various cities on a map. The distance on the map is measured by using paper clips. Each paper clip is equal to about 465 actual miles.

1. How can you calculate the actual distance, in miles, between two cities using the information provided in the table?

____

____

2. What is the actual distance between Seattle, WA and Wichita, KS? Use place-value blocks or draw an array to find the partial products. Then find the actual distance in miles.

3. **Extension** Jackie and Hannah traveled from Boise to Phoenix, and then from Phoenix to Philadelphia. Jackie calculated the total distance in miles by multiplying each distance measured with paper clips by 465, then adding the two products. Hannah calculated the total distance in miles by adding the two distances on the map measured with paper clips, then multiplying the sum by 465. Which strategy to find the distance is correct? Explain.

____

____

____

Name ______________________________

Topographic Maps

Did You Know? A topographic map is a type of map that shows the elevation of features of the Earth. Topographic maps use curved lines to show the elevation of a mountain. Look at the diagram to the right. Imagine cutting a mountain into different layers. Each layer is a specific distance apart. The outline of the mountain at each layer is shown on the topographic map.

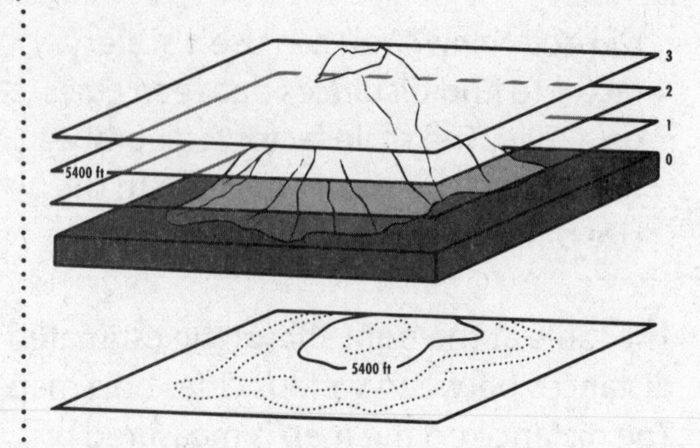

A geological surveyor created this topographical map showing the elevation of two different mountains. Each layer (A–E) represents an elevation of 2,860 feet.

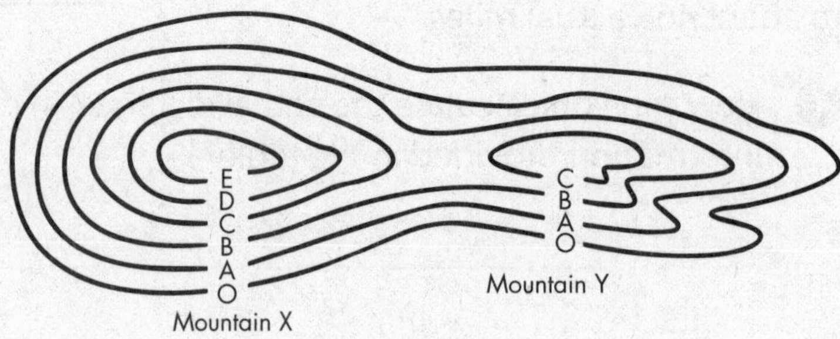

1. Sea level is represented on the map by the layer labeled O. Explain how to determine the elevation represented by layer A.

____

____

2. Write an addition equation and a multiplication equation to represent the elevation represented by layer B.

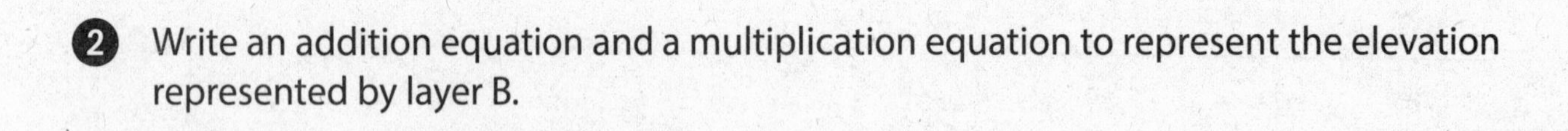

____

____

3. The elevation represented by layer C is ________ feet.

4. **Extension** Which mountain has a greater elevation? Explain.

____

____

Name ______________________________

Daily Review
3-1

1. Which shows 98,732 rounded to the ten thousands place?

Ⓐ 10,000
Ⓑ 99,000
Ⓒ 100,000
Ⓓ 1,000,000

2. Which is the number name for 73,922?

Ⓐ Seventy-three thousand, nine hundred twenty-two
Ⓑ Seventy-three thousand, ninety-two
Ⓒ Seventy thousand, nine hundred two
Ⓓ Seventy thousand, three hundred ninety-two

3. There are 17,000 people registered for the hip-hop dance marathon. Only 10,730 dancers registered for the square dance marathon. How many more people registered for the hip-hop dance marathon?

Ⓐ 7,730 people
Ⓑ 6,270 people
Ⓒ 6,000 people
Ⓓ 5,270 people

4. Shari has 1,592 stamps in her collection. How many stamps does Shari have, rounded to the nearest thousand?

Ⓐ 1,590 Ⓒ 2,000
Ⓑ 1,600 Ⓓ 20,000

5. A total of 103,985 fans attended the baseball game on Saturday, and a total of 103,667 attended the game on Sunday. Use $>$ or $<$ to compare the attendances. On which day did more fans attend the game?

____
____
____

6. A bushel can contain 149,637 soybeans or 81,183 kernels of corn. Jackson says there are 48,454 more soybeans than kernels of corn per bushel. Use rounding to estimate the difference. Explain if Jackson's answer is reasonable.

____
____
____
____
____
____
____

7. Write 804,082 in expanded form.

____
____

Name ______________________________

Reteach to Build Understanding
3-1

Vocabulary

1. The **Associative Property of Multiplication** states that factors can be grouped differently and the product remains the same. Changing the grouping of the factors changes the factors that are multiplied first.

   Use the Associative Property of Multiplication to find 2×30.

   $2 \times 30 = 2 \times (3 \times 10)$ — Break apart 30.

   $= (2 \times$ ______ $) \times$ ______ — Group the factors of the basic fact.

   $=$ ______ $\times 10$ — Multiply the factors inside the parentheses.

   $=$ ______ — Find the product.

2. A **multiple** is the product of a given factor and any whole number.

   Find the next three multiples in each number pattern.

   Multiples of 10: 10, 20, 30, ______, ______, ______

   Multiples of 100: 100, 200, 300, ______, ______, ______

Use place value and the Associative Property of Multiplication to find the product.

3. $4 \times 600 = 4 \times$ ______ hundreds — Use place value.

   $= ($ ______ $\times$ ______ $)$ __________ — Group the factors in a different way.

   $=$ ______ $\times 100$ — Find the product inside the parentheses.

   $=$ __________ — Find the final product. Think: 24×1, and then write final product.

Use place value to find the product.

4. $6 \times 50 = 6 \times 5$ tens

   $= 30$ __________

   $=$ __________

5. $6 \times 6{,}000 = 6 \times 6$ __________

   $= 36$ __________

   $=$ __________

On the Back!

6. Explain how you can use the basic fact $4 \times 8 = 32$ and place value to help find 4×80, 4×800, and $4 \times 8{,}000$.

Name ______________________________

Build Mathematical Literacy
3-1

Read the problem. Answer the questions to help understand the problem.

Higher Order Thinking Tina visited Funland with her mom and a friend. They bought tickets for Plan C. How much money did they save on the two children's tickets for Plan C instead of buying separate tickets for Plan A and Plan B?

DATA

Funland Ticket Prices

Plans	Adult	Child
Plan A Waterpark	$30	$20
Plan B Amusement Park	$40	$30
Plan C Combined A + B	$60	$40

Interpret the table

1. What does the first column in the table show?

____

2. What do the second and third columns in the table show?

____

Use the data in the table

3. What data from the table should you use to find the money that they would spend on children's tickets using Plan C?

____

4. What data from the table should you use to find the money that they would spend on children's tickets using Plan A? Plan B?

____

5. Will you need to use all of the data in the table to answer the question? Explain.

____

____

Name ____________________

Enrichment 3-1

Decode and Solve

Use number sense to decode the value of each shape.

1. 6 × = 480
2. × = 640
3. × = 720
4. × =
5. × 200 = 1,000
6. × = 3,000
7. × = 1,200
8. × =

= ____ = ____ = ____ = ____

= ____ = ____ = ____ = ____

Use the value of the shapes that you decoded above to solve these number sentences.

9. × = ____
10. × = ____
11. × = ____
12. × = ____
13. × = ____
14. × = ____
15. × × = ____

Name ______________________

Daily Review
3-2

1. The Earth rotates around the sun at an average speed of 1,000 miles per hour. About how many miles does the Earth travel in 8 hours?

Ⓐ About 80,000 miles
Ⓑ About 8,000 miles
Ⓒ About 800 miles
Ⓓ About 80 miles

2. A radio station held an online cutest dog contest for 3 days. Aleesa entered her dog Teddy's picture. The first day of the contest Teddy received 1,486 votes, the second day Teddy received 1,677 votes, and the third day 945 votes. How many votes did Teddy receive?

Ⓐ 3,163 votes
Ⓑ 4,063 votes
Ⓒ 4,108 votes
Ⓓ 5,108 votes

3. One school collects 2,040 pounds of newspaper during a newspaper recycling drive. Another school collects 1,860 pounds. Use mental math to find how many pounds of newspaper the two schools collect in all.

Ⓐ 3,080 pounds
Ⓑ 3,090 pounds
Ⓒ 3,900 pounds
Ⓓ 4,000 pounds

4. Penny's family wants to buy a house that costs $180,599. The family also will need to pay additional fees of $7,685. What is the total cost for the house and the fees?

____

5. Look at the table below. Write the name of the county that raised the most money for education and the name of the county that raised the least money. Then explain how you decided.

Money Raised for Education

County	Amount Raised
Pleasantville	$287,623
Woodlane	$285,935
East Shore	$321,961
Forest Hill	$305,689

____
____
____
____
____
____
____
____

Name ______________________________

Reteach to Build Understanding
3-2

Vocabulary

1. **Rounding** is a process that determines which multiple of 10, 100, 1,000, and so on a number is closest to.

Round 3,524 to the nearest thousand.

Look at the digit to the right of the thousands place.

Add 1 to the digit in the rounding place. Then write 3 zeros.

3,524 rounded to the nearest thousand is ________.

Rounding Rules		
If the digit to the right of the rounding place is:	First,	Then,
less than 5	Keep the digit in the rounding place the same.	Change all of the digits to the right of the rounding place to zeros.
8,453	→	8,000
5 or greater	Add 1 to the digit in the rounding place.	Change all of the digits to the right of the rounding place to zeros.
8,543	→	9,000

Use rounding to estimate 6 × 789.

2. Round 789 to the nearest hundred. ________

6 × ________ = ________

Use rounding to estimate 4 × 6,251.

3. Round 6,251 to the nearest thousand. ________

________ × ________ = ________

You can also use rounding to check if a product is reasonable.

Check if 5 × 3,011 = 15,055 is reasonable.

4. Round 3,011 to the nearest thousand. ________

________ × ________ = ________

5 × 3,011 is about ________.

15,055 is close to ________, so the answer is ________.

On the Back!

5. Estimate the product of 7 × 417 by using rounding.

Name ______________________________

Build Mathematical Literacy
3-2

Read the problem. Answer the questions to help understand the problem.

Higher Order Thinking An adult sleeps about 480 minutes per day. An infant sleeps about 820 minutes per day. About how many more minutes does an infant sleep than an adult in one week?

Solve the problem two different ways.

1. What is the given information that will be used to solve the problem?

____

____

2. What is the question asking you to find?

____

____

3. Are the units in the given information the same as the units in the question? Explain.

____

____

____

4. Write two other questions that you need to answer before you can answer the question in the problem.

____

____

5. What operation will you need to use to answer the questions that you wrote?

____

6. How could you solve the problem without answering the questions that you wrote for Exercise 4?

____

____

Name ____________________

Who's Here?

Do you know how to find the attendance of people at a large event? There are too many people to count one by one, so you need to estimate. This is called crowd estimation.

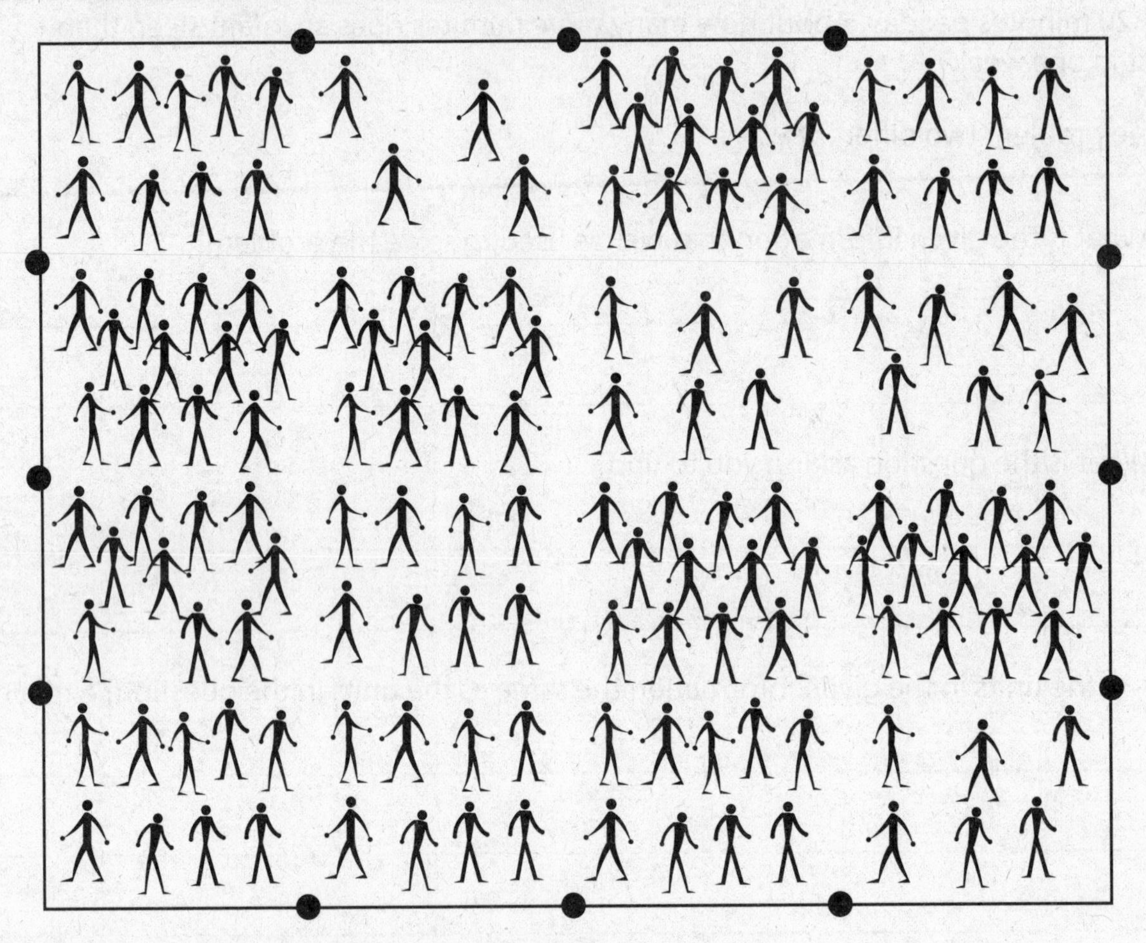

1. Draw 3 lines top to bottom by connecting dot to dot. Draw 3 lines going across by connecting dot to dot. Find the box that is farthest left and on the bottom. Count as many people in the box as you can. ____________

2. Estimate to find the total number of people.

   number of people × number of boxes = total number of people

Name ____________________

Daily Review
3-3

1. Which numbers have a digit in the ten thousands place that is 10 times as great as the value of the digit in the thousands place?

- ☐ 877,876
- ☐ 770,605
- ☐ 545,541
- ☐ 333,213
- ☐ 55,120

2. One day a year 10 schools gather to compete in track and field events. Each school is represented by 8 teams of 5 students each. How many students compete?

Ⓐ 800 students
Ⓑ 500 students
Ⓒ 400 students
Ⓓ 40 students

3. Last year, three classes collected canned goods for a food drive. One class collected 738 cans of food. Another class collected 981 cans. The third class collected 850 cans. How many cans of food were collected in all?

Ⓐ 2,479 cans
Ⓑ 2,560 cans
Ⓒ 2,569 cans
Ⓓ 2,579 cans

4. If there are 4 quarters in one dollar, how many quarters are in 500 dollars?

____

5. Write the number name for 832,009.

____

____

6. Use place-value strategies and relationships to write the number that is 1,000 times greater than the product of 1×5.

____

7. Find the difference. Then use the inverse operation to check your solution.

$$\begin{array}{r} 74{,}836 \\ -\ 56{,}775 \\ \hline \square\square{,}\square\square\square \end{array}$$

8. Write a comparison for 14,278 and 41,728. Use $>$, $=$, or $<$.

____

____

Name ______________________________

Vocabulary

1. **Partial products** are the products found by multiplying each place value of one factor by another factor.

   The model shows 4 × 125.

   To find the partial products, multiply the number of groups (4) by

   the ones: 4 × 5 = ________

   the tens: 4 × 20 = ________

   the hundreds: 4 × 100 = ________.

   Add the partial products to find the product.

   ________ + ________ + ________ = ________

   So, 4 × 125 = ________.

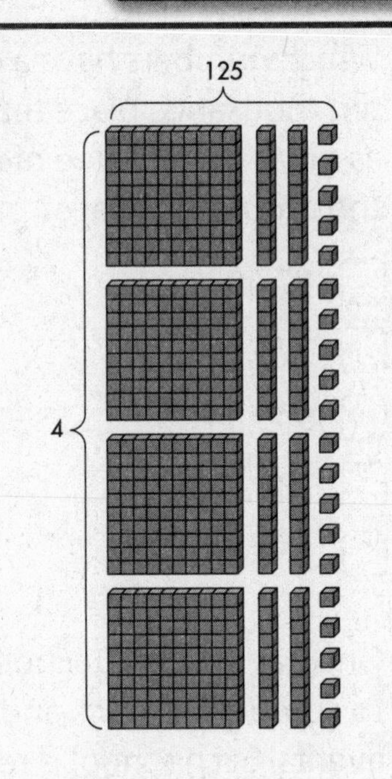

Use the array to show 5 × 137.

137 = 100 + 30 + 7

5

2. Complete the array on the right.

Use the array to find the partial products.

3. 5 × 7 = ________

   5 × 30 = ________

   5 × 100 = ________

Complete the calculation.

4. 5 × 137 = ________

On the Back!

5. Draw an array to show 123 × 5. Use the partial products to complete the calculation.

Name ______________________

Read the problem. Answer the questions to help understand the problem.

Model with Math What multiplication equation do the place-value blocks show? Find the product. Then write a problem that could be solved using this model.

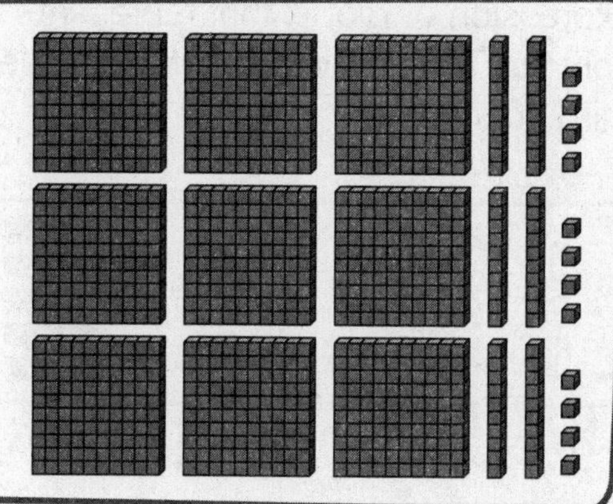

1. Multiplication is repeated addition. How does this relationship help you know what to look for in the place-value blocks?

____

2. Does each column of place-value blocks show the same value? Explain.

____

____

3. Does each row of place-value blocks show the same value? Explain.

____

4. What part of a multiplication equation is the product? Circle the place-value blocks that represent the product.

____

____

5. Circle the top row of blocks. Name something that these blocks could represent in a real-world problem.

____

____

6. Using your answer to Exercise 5, what would all of the place-value blocks shown represent in the same real-world problem?

____

Name ______________________________

Enrichment
3-3

Multiplication Match

Draw lines to match each expression in the first column to the expression or model that represents the same problem in the second column. Then draw a line from the second column to the product in the third column.

1. 2 × 23	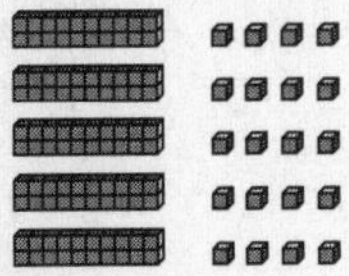	120
2. 3 × 231	(6 × 10) + (6 × 9)	452
3. 3 × 18	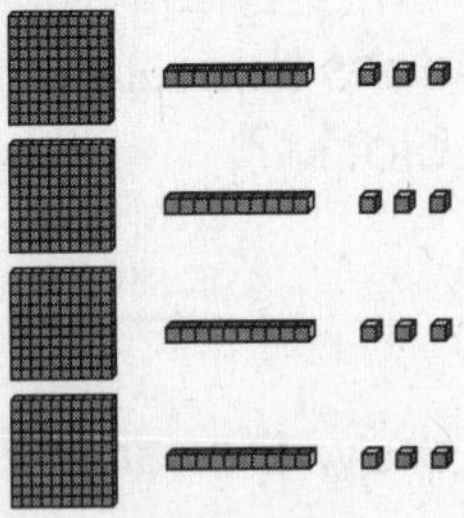	117
4. 4 × 18	(3 × 200) + (3 × 30) + (3 × 1)	234
5. 5 × 24	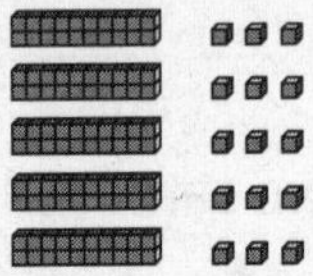	48
6. 6 × 39	(3 × 30) + (3 × 9)	68
7. 4 × 17		72
8. 4 × 113	(4 × 10) + (4 × 8)	115
9. 3 × 39	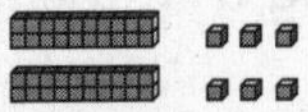	114
10. 5 × 23	(2 × 20) + (2 × 4)	693
11. 2 × 24	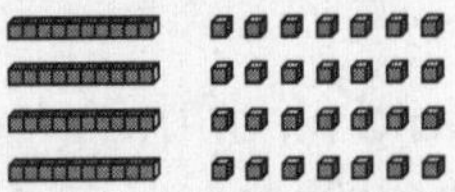	46
12. 6 × 19	(6 × 30) + (6 × 9)	54

Name ______________________

Daily Review

3-4

1. Which factors have a product of 40,000?

Ⓐ 5×80

Ⓑ 5×800

Ⓒ $5 \times 8{,}000$

Ⓓ $5 \times 80{,}000$

2. On Friday, 6,358 people went to the fair. On Saturday, 7,823 people went to the fair. How many more people went to the fair on Saturday than on Friday?

Ⓐ 1,465 people

Ⓑ 1,565 people

Ⓒ 13,181 people

Ⓓ 14,181 people

3. There are 5,280 feet in one mile. Estimate how many feet are in 4 miles.

Ⓐ about 2,000 feet

Ⓑ about 5,000 feet

Ⓒ about 20,000 feet

Ⓓ about 200,000 feet

4. Which numbers round to 460,000 when rounded to the nearest ten thousand? Select all that apply.

☐ 471,679

☐ 465,544

☐ 462,984

☐ 456,952

☐ 454,035

5. Write 67,103 in expanded form.

____

____

____

6. A community sponsored a race for charity. 1,235 participants registered before the day of the race. 340 registered the day of the race. On the day of the race 49 participants did not show up. How many participants took part in the race? Write and solve equations.

____

____

____

____

7. The table shows the number of books in the school library for certain genres. Estimate the total number of books in all four genres.

Genre	Number of Books
Adventure	493
Fantasy	272
Mystery	521
Science Fiction	624

____

____

Name ______________________________

Reteach to Build Understanding

3-4

Vocabulary

1. A **numerical expression** contains numbers and at least one operation.

   Which of the following are numerical expressions? Write Yes or No.

   5,178 ________ 6×80 ________

   $26 - 15 + 4$ ________ $77 = 77$ ________

2. The **Distributive Property** says that multiplying a sum (or difference) by a number is the same as multiplying each number in the sum (or difference) by that number and adding (or subtracting) the products.

   Use the Distributive Property to rewrite 3×546.

   $3 \times 546 = 3 \times (500 +$ ________ $+$ ________$)$ Break apart 546.

   $= (3 \times$ ________$) + (3 \times$ ________$) + (3 \times$ ________$)$ Distribute the 3 to each addend.

3. $4 \times 613 = 4 \times ($________ $+$ ________ $+$ ________$)$ Break apart 613.

   $= ($________ $\times 600) + ($________ $\times 10) + ($________ $\times 3)$ Distribute the 4.

   $=$ ________ $+$ ________ $+$ ________ Multiply. Then add.

   $=$ ________

4. $5 \times 792 = 5 \times (800 -$ ________$)$ Use compatible numbers.

   $= (5 \times$ ________$) - (5 \times$ ________$)$ Distribute the 5.

   $=$ ________ $-$ ________ Multiply. Then subtract.

   $=$ ________

On the Back!

5. Use the Distributive Property to find 6×296.

Name ______________________________

Build Mathematical Literacy
3-4

Read the problem. Answer the questions to help understand the problem.

Higher Order Thinking Todd Mountain is a mountain peak near Tyler, Texas. A ranger hiked 607 feet to and from the peak, each way. The ranger hiked 3 times in the past four weeks. How far did the ranger hike on Todd Mountain over the past four weeks?

1. Underline the information that you know you will need to use to solve the problem.

____

2. Why are the words *each way* an important part of the given information?

____

____

____

____

3. Circle any information that you do **NOT** need to use to solve the problem.

____

4. Explain why the information you circled is not needed to solve the problem.

____

____

5. What exactly does this problem ask you to find?

____

6. What strategy or operations will you use to solve the problem?

____

____

____

Name ______________________

Enrichment
3-4

Mathematical Marlena

Marlena is about to amaze you with great feats of mathematics. Marlena says, "I want you to write the number 37 three times."

1. Now she says, "Multiply the first 37 by 1." ______
2. Then she tells you, "Multiply the second 37 by 2." ______
3. She directs you to "Multiply the third 37 by 3." ______
4. She says, "Take each product and multiply it by 3."

____

____

5. Marlena now asks, "What is the pattern if you continue to multiply 3 times the product of 37 and the next number in sequence?"

____

____

____

Then Marlena begins her second math game.

6. She tells you, "Write a number between 1 and 5." ______
7. Then she says, "Now add 5 to the number." ______
8. Now she says, "Multiply the number by 2." ______
9. She says, "Subtract 2 from the product." ______
10. Marlena then says, "Now multiply that answer by 2." ______
11. Then she asks you to "Divide the product by 4." ______
12. She finally directs you to "Subtract 4 from your answer." ______

Marlena says, "The answer is the number you wrote down!"

Name ______________________________

Daily Review
3-5

1. Which comparison is true?

Ⓐ 26,931 < 26,073

Ⓑ 48,326 > 48,439

Ⓒ 318,846 > 319,432

Ⓓ 647,825 < 749,968

2. Will had 4,260 messages in his email inbox. He deleted some of the messages. He now has 3,506 messages in his inbox. How many messages did Will delete?

Ⓐ 7,766 messages

Ⓑ 1,006 messages

Ⓒ 754 messages

Ⓓ 654 messages

3. Each month, Factory A produces 2,005 widgets and Factory B produces 2,020 widgets. How many widgets do both factories produce in 3 months?

Ⓐ 4,025 widgets

Ⓑ 8,050 widgets

Ⓒ 12,075 widgets

Ⓓ 24,150 widgets

4. Which is equal to 110,000 + 400 + 30 + 4?

Ⓐ 11,434

Ⓑ 110,434

Ⓒ 111,434

Ⓓ 114,340

5. Explain how to use partial products to find 3 × 39.

____

____

____

____

____

6. Photos-To-Go printed 2,000 copies of a brochure for a travel agency. The brochure included 5 photos of popular vacation destinations. How many photos are in all of the printed brochures? Write your equation.

____

____

____

7. How do you estimate the sum of 198,260 + 31, 900?

____

____

____

____

Name ______________________________

Reteach to Build Understanding
3-5

Vocabulary

1. An area model helps you visualize the partial products needed to find the product of two factors.

   Find 7 × 483. Multiply each place value to find the partial products.

   7 × 3 = ________

   7 × 80 = ________

   7 × 400 = ________

   400 +80+3
   7

   Add the partial products to find the final product.

   ________ + ________ + ________ = ________

2. You can use rounding to **estimate** or find a number that is close.

   Round 483 to estimate the product.

   7 × ________ = ________

Use partial products and an area to find the product.

3.
```
    6 2 5
  ×     3
  _,___
     __
  +  __
  _,___
```

   600 +20+5
   3

   How many hundreds? Think 3 × 600.
   How many tens? Think 3 × 20.
   How many ones? Think 3 × 5.

   Add the partial products to find the product.

4. Use rounding to estimate 3 × 625.

   ____

5. Is your answer to Exercise 3 reasonable?

   ____

   ____

On the Back!

6. Draw an area model and use partial products to find 913 × 7. Check if your answer is reasonable.

Name ______________________________

Build Mathematical Literacy
3-5

Read the problem below. Then write if the statement is True or False. For each statement that is false, explain why using details from the text.

There are usually 365 days in each year. Every fourth year is called a leap year and has one extra day in February. How many days are there in 8 years if 2 of the years are leap years?

1. Every year has exactly 365 days.

____

____

2. A leap year has 4 extra days.

____

____

3. A leap year has a total of 366 days.

____

____

4. You can find the number of days in 8 years using the expression 365×8.

____

____

5. The expression 366×2 represents the number of days in 2 leap years.

____

____

6. The solution to the problem will tell how many days are in 2 leap years.

____

____

Name ______________________________

Enrichment
3-5

Partial Product Pick

Circle the partial products for each problem.

1. 379×9

81	270	810	63
27	630	2,700	8,100

2. 446×8

32	160	48	3,200
480	320	3,600	3,500

3. $1,937 \times 6$

180	42	540	60
480	320	6,000	5,400

4. $1,251 \times 7$

70	14	7	1,000
350	7,000	35	1,400

5. $9,033 \times 6$

600	54	18	5,400
1,800	54,000	540	180

6. $6,565 \times 4$

200	24,000	20	20,000
240	24	2,400	2,000

Name ________________________________

Daily Review
3-6

1. Find 8,365 − 1,174.

Ⓐ 6,191
Ⓑ 7,181
Ⓒ 7,191
Ⓓ 7,291

2. A bank bag holds 6,245 pennies. What is 6,245 rounded to the nearest hundred?

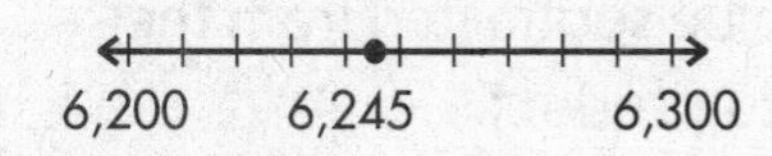

Ⓐ 7,000
Ⓑ 6,300
Ⓒ 6,250
Ⓓ 6,200

3. Which comparison is true if 1,426 replaces the box?

Ⓐ 1,326 > ☐
Ⓑ ☐ < 1,467
Ⓒ 1,624 < ☐
Ⓓ ☐ = 1,462

4. Which shows breaking apart the expression 6 × 52 using the Distributive Property?

Ⓐ (6 + 50) + (6 + 2)
Ⓑ (6 × 50) + (6 × 20)
Ⓒ (6 × 50) + 2
Ⓓ (6 × 50) + (6 × 2)

5. The Pilgrims sailed aboard the Mayflower to America in 1620. In 2040, how many years will have passed since the Pilgrims sailed to America?

____

6. There are 3,946 adults, 4,137 children, and 378 dogs living in a town. How many people live in the town?

____

7. Tonya used partial products to solve the problem below. Tonya's answer is not correct. Explain Tonya's error. What is the correct product?

$$\begin{array}{r} 547 \\ \times \quad 6 \\ \hline 42 \\ 240 \\ +\ 300 \\ \hline 582 \end{array}$$

____

____

____

____

____

____

Name ______________________________

Reteach to Build Understanding
3-6

Vocabulary

1. **Compensation** is a mental-math strategy. To use compensation, choose numbers that are close to the numbers in the problem, to make the computation easier, and then adjust the answer.

Use compensation to find 3×58.

Think: 60 is close to 58. Find 3×60 and adjust the answer.

$3 \times 60 =$ ________

$3 \times 2 = 6$

Think: Since 60 is 2 more than 58, the estimate is greater than the actual product. Multiply 3 by 2 to determine the amount that needs to be subtracted from the estimated product.

Adjust the answer by subtracting ________.

$180 -$ ________ $=$ ________

So, $3 \times 58 =$ ________.

2. Use compensation to find 6×302.

Think: 302 is close to 300. Find 6×300 and adjust the answer.

$6 \times 300 =$ ________

$6 \times 2 = 12$

Think: Since 300 is 2 less than 302, the estimate is less than the actual product. Multiply 6 by 2 to determine the amount that needs to be added to the estimated product.

Adjust the answer by adding ________.

$1{,}800 +$ ________ $=$ ________

3. Use compensation to find 4×252.

$4 \times 250 =$ ________ $\quad 4 \times 2 =$ ________

$1{,}000 +$ ________ $=$ ________

4. Use compensation to find 2×895.

$2 \times 900 =$ ________ $\quad 2 \times 5 =$ ________

$1{,}800 -$ ________ $=$ ________

5. Use compensation to find 8×998. ________

On the Back!

6. Use compensation to find 8×115.

Name ______________________________

Build Mathematical Literacy
3-6

Read the problem. Answer the questions to help understand the problem.

Higher Order Thinking Do you think it would be better to use breaking apart or compensation to find the product of 5 × 328? Explain why and show how to find the product.

1. Underline the names of the two multiplication strategies mentioned in the problem.

____

2. Define each strategy.

Strategy 1: ______________________________

____

____

Strategy 2: ______________________________

____

____

3. Explain how you could use each strategy to find the product 5 × 328.

Strategy 1: ______________________________

____

Strategy 2: ______________________________

____

4. Which strategy will you choose to solve the problem? Explain.

____

____

____

____

Name ______________________

Enrichment **3-6**

Multiply Without a Pencil

You know different methods you can use to find products.
Try to solve the problems below in your head.
If you find the solution mentally, circle *MM* for *mental math.*
If you need to write out the solution, circle *PP* for *paper and pencil.*

1. Fred drove on Interstate 95 for 4 hours. He went 55 miles an hour the whole time. How many miles did he drive?

____

MM or PP

2. Celie read 6 chapters of a mystery on Saturday. Each chapter had 25 pages. How many pages did Celie read that day?

____

MM or PP

3. Darius practiced his guitar 15 minutes a day for 7 days. How many minutes did Darius spend practicing guitar that week?

____

MM or PP

4. A baker makes 72 cookies per batch. At that rate, how many cookies would the baker make in 3 batches?

____

MM or PP

5. Eleni does 40 sit-ups every morning before she gets ready for school. How many sit-ups will Eleni do in 5 days?

____

MM or PP

6. A large bag of dry dog food weighs 30 pounds. What is the total weight of 4 large bags of dry dog food?

____

MM or PP

7. A bag of gravel weighs 45 pounds. What is the total weight of 4 bags of gravel?

____

MM or PP

8. A crate of melons weighs 50 pounds. What is the total weight of 5 crates of melons?

____

MM or PP

9. There are 52 cards in a standard deck of playing cards. How many cards would be in 6 standard decks?

____

MM or PP

10. A piano has 88 keys. Some are white and some are black. How many keys would there be on 5 pianos?

____

MM or PP

11. Which problems were easiest to solve in your head? Which ones were harder for you to do mentally? Explain.

____

Name ______________________

Daily Review
3-7

1. When rounded to the nearest thousand, which number rounds to 64,000?

Ⓐ 664,320
Ⓑ 164,126
Ⓒ 64,501
Ⓓ 64,486

2. Juan read 6 books in a series on American heroes. Each book had 96 pages. Then Juan read 4 books on famous scientists. Each of those books had 56 pages. Which is the most reasonable estimate of the total number of pages Juan read?

Ⓐ About 150 pages
Ⓑ About 600 pages
Ⓒ About 840 pages
Ⓓ About 1,500 pages

3. Which pairs represent the same number? Select all that apply.

☐ one hundred thousand, thirty-two; 132,000
☐ ninety-two thousand, five hundred one; 92,501
☐ seventy-four thousand, nineteen; 74,190
☐ six thousand, seventy; 6,070
☐ three hundred six thousand; 300,600

4. A city is selling tickets for Family Night at the ballpark. Tickets cost $5 each. On Monday, 517 tickets were sold. On Tuesday, 383 tickets were sold. How much money has been collected for the tickets?

____

5. The Red Caboose sells 745 different model trains. On each model train there are 8 wheels. Explain how to use rounding to estimate the total number of wheels on the model trains.

____

____

____

____

6. The table below shows the number of students enrolled in four elementary schools. Which school has the most students?

District Enrollment

School	Number of Students
Adams	4,341
Braintree	4,322
Clark	4,371
Dumont	4,327

____

Name ______________________________

Reteach to Build Understanding
3-7

Vocabulary

1. A **product** is the answer to a multiplication problem. Use the Distributive Property to solve the problem in smaller pieces.

$5 \times 6{,}839 = 5 \times (\_\_\_\_\_\_ + 30 + 9)$ Rewrite the greater number in expanded form.

$= (5 \times 6{,}000) + (5 \times \_\_\_\_) + (5 \times \_\_\_\_) + (5 \times \_\_\_\_)$ The Distributive Property means that you can multiply first, then add, and not change the value.

$= \_\_\_\_\_\_ + 4{,}000 + \_\_\_\_\_\_$ Multiply.

$= \_\_\_\_\_\_$ Add.

2. Use estimation to check if your answer above is reasonable. Estimate the product of $5 \times 6{,}839$.

Round 6,839 to the nearest thousand. ________

Estimate the product:

$5 \times \_\_\_\_\_\_ = \_\_\_\_\_\_$

3. Is your answer to Exercise 1 reasonable? Explain.

____

4. Find the product of $9 \times 4{,}235$.

____

5. Use estimation to check if your answer above is reasonable.

Estimate the product:

$9 \times \_\_\_\_\_\_ = \_\_\_\_\_\_$

6. Is your answer to Exercise 4 reasonable? ________

On the Back!

7. Find the product of $4 \times 1{,}875$. Estimate to check if your answer is reasonable.

Name ______________________________

Build Mathematical Literacy
3-7

Read the problem. Answer the questions to help understand the problem.

Higher Order Thinking On Monday, Paolo sold 21 tickets to the dance. On Tuesday, he sold three times as many tickets as he sold on Monday. On Wednesday, he sold twice as many tickets as he sold on Tuesday. How many total tickets did Paolo sell in the three days?

1. Does the problem tell you how many tickets Paolo sold Monday, Tuesday and Wednesday? Explain.

____

____

____

2. What other questions do you need to answer before you can find out how many tickets Paolo sold in 3 days?

____

____

3. What information from the problem do you need to use find out how many tickets Paolo sold on Tuesday?

____

____

4. What information from the problem do you need to use to find out how many tickets Paolo sold on Wednesday?

____

____

5. To find out how many tickets Paolo sold on Wednesday, what information do you need that is NOT given in the problem?

____

Name ______________________________

Enrichment
3-7

Rhyming Multiplication

Write a number sentence for each verse.

1. As I was going to the store
I saw seven dogs and one dog more.
Each dog had fifteen bones to chew.
How many bones came into view?

____

2. 18 marchers marched in a row.
Each marcher had 4 horns to blow.
They blew all the horns, both big and small.
How many horns did they blow in all?

____

3. Six monkeys were kind of thrifty.
They all loved bananas and they each ate fifty.
Bananas to monkeys are a special treat.
How many bananas did the monkeys eat?

____

4. What did I see on the street today?
Seventy-seven fire trucks came my way.
Nine firefighters on each truck waved at me.
How many firefighters did I see?

____

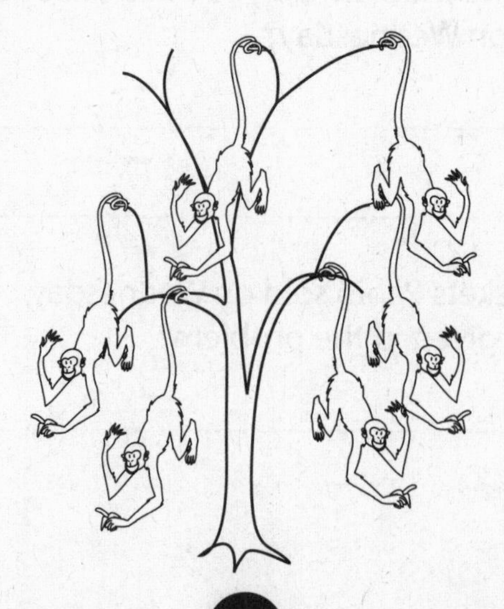

Name ________________________________

Daily Review
3-8

1. In which number is the value of the digit in the thousands place ten times as great as the value of the digit in the hundreds place?

Ⓐ 200,200
Ⓑ 200,100
Ⓒ 2,200
Ⓓ 2,100

2. Find 600 − 443.

Ⓐ 157
Ⓑ 167
Ⓒ 257
Ⓓ 267

3. The Arctic tern migrates 71,000 kilometers each year. The sooty shearwater migrates 64,373 kilometers each year. How much farther does the Arctic tern migrate than the sooty shearwater?

Ⓐ 7,737 kilometers
Ⓑ 7,626 kilometers
Ⓒ 6,737 kilometers
Ⓓ 6,627 kilometers

4. Which expression can help you find 4 × 800?

Ⓐ 48 × 100
Ⓑ 4 × 1,000
Ⓒ 8 × 100
Ⓓ 4 × 8

5. Use the symbol >, =, or < to make the statement true.

102,732 ◯ 103,832

6. Each year a zoo buys 62,853 mealworms, 75,194 waxworms, and 81,407 earthworms to feed some of the animals. How many worms does the zoo buy each year?

____

7. Find 2 × 132. Use a drawing to help. Explain the steps you used to find your answer.

____
____
____
____
____
____
____
____
____
____
____

Name ______________________

Vocabulary

1. One way to model with math is to use a representation, like a picture or diagram, to help solve a problem. You can then model the math by writing an equation. An **equation** is a number sentence that uses the equal sign (=) to show that two expressions have the same value.

   Look at the bar diagram.

125				
25	25	25	25	25

   There are ________ equal groups. Each group is labeled with ________. There are ________ in all.

   Write an equation for the bar diagram.

   $5 \times$ ________ $=$ ________

Complete each bar diagram. Then write and solve an equation to answer the question.

2. There are 245 parking spaces on each floor of a parking garage. The parking garage has 5 floors. How many parking spaces does the garage have?

   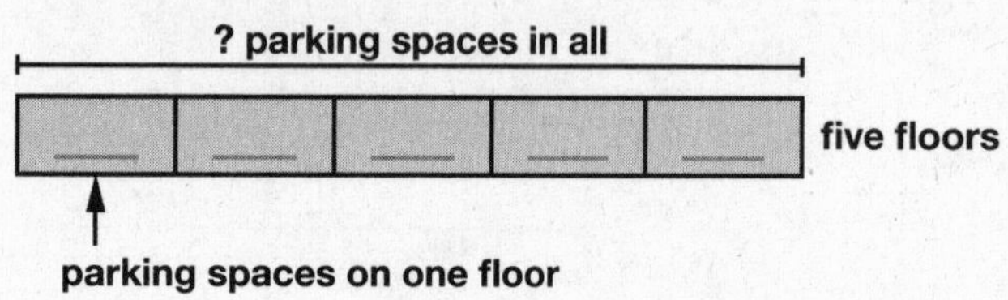

   $$\begin{array}{r} 245 \\ \times \quad 5 \\ \hline \square,\square\square\square \end{array}$$

   There are ________ parking spaces.

3. Each classroom has 28 students. There are 8 classrooms. How many students are in the classrooms?

   ? students in all

   eight classrooms

   students in each classroom

   $$\begin{array}{r} 28 \\ \times \quad 8 \\ \hline \square\square\square \end{array}$$

   There are ________ students.

On the Back!

4. Nyla earns $208 a day. She works 5 days a week. How much does Nyla earn each week? Draw a picture and write an equation to solve.

Name ______________________________

Build Mathematical Literacy
3-8

Read each sentence of the problem, then complete the steps to draw a picture and write an equation that represents the problem.

Model with Math Annie has 6 albums of stamps in her stamp collection. Each album contains 440 stamps. How many stamps does Annie have in her collection?

Draw a picture and write an equation to represent the problem.

Read the first sentence of the problem.

1. Make a simple drawing to represent the first sentence.

____

2. Circle the numerical information in the first sentence. Write as much of the equation as you can using this information.

____

Read the second sentence of the problem.

3. Add to the drawing you created in Exercise 1 to represent the information give in the second sentence.

____

4. Circle the numerical information in the second sentence. Underline any words that are a clue to the operation. Add the operation and number to the equation.

____

Read the third sentence of the problem.

5. How can you use your drawing to answer the question?

____

____

____

6. Use the answer to the question to complete your equation.

____

Name ______________________

Roll Out the Fun

Find the missing factors or products to complete each equation.
Then complete the sentences in the word problems.

Zippy Roller Coaster
Height: 114 ft
Length: 2,711 ft

Souvenirs
Baseball cap—157 tickets
Stuffed animal—318 tickets

1. Neil's family and Reena's family spent two days at the amusement park. On Fridays, family passes cost $119. On Saturdays, family passes cost $139.

$2 \times 119 =$ __________ $2 \times 139 =$ __________

In all, the two families spent __________ on Friday

and __________ on Saturday.

2. The world's longest roller coaster is 3 times the length of the Zippy roller coaster. The world's tallest roller coaster is 4 times the height of the Zippy roller coaster.

__________ $\times 3 =$ __________ $114 \times$ __________ $=$ __________

The world's longest roller coaster is __________ feet long.

The world's tallest roller coaster is __________ feet high.

3. Before leaving the amusement park, Reena went to the souvenir store to trade in her tickets. She chose 1 baseball cap for each of her 3 friends. Then she chose 2 stuffed animals for herself.

__________ $\times 157 =$ __________ $2 \times$ __________ $=$ __________

Reena used __________ tickets to get gifts for her friends

and __________ tickets to get the stuffed animals.

Name ______________________________

Use Strategies and Properties to Multiply by 2-Digit Numbers

Dear Family,

Your child is learning how to multiply 2-digit numbers by 2-digit numbers. Some of the strategies he or she is learning to use include arrays and partial products. Below are examples for 13×25.

Use an array.
Add each part of the array to find the product.

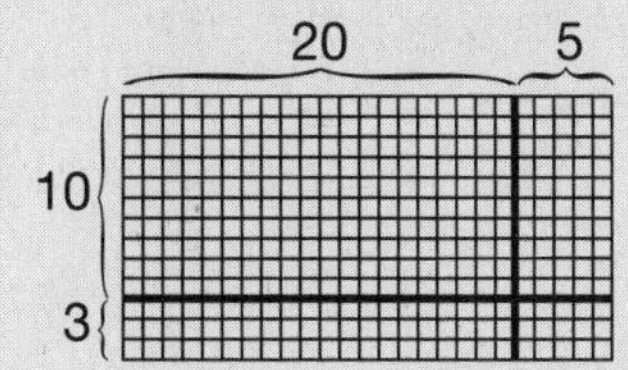

$10 \times 20 = 200$
$10 \times 5 = 50$
$3 \times 20 = 60$
$3 \times 5 = 15$
325

Use place value and partial products.
Multiply the ones, then the tens.
Add the partial products.

$$\begin{array}{r} 25 \\ \times 13 \\ \hline 15 \\ 60 \\ 50 \\ +200 \\ \hline 325 \end{array}$$

15, 60: Multiply the ones.
50, 200: Multiply the tens.
325: Add the partial products.

Multiplying Game

Materials number cube (labeled 1–6)

Play in pairs. Each player rolls the number cube. Record the number the first player rolls in the tens place and the number the second player rolls in the ones place to create a 2-digit number. Each player rolls the number cube again, recording the numbers in the same way. Then players complete the multiplication. When a player has found the answer, he or she says "Done." The other player checks the answer. If it is correct, he or she receives a point. The first player to earn 3 points wins the game.

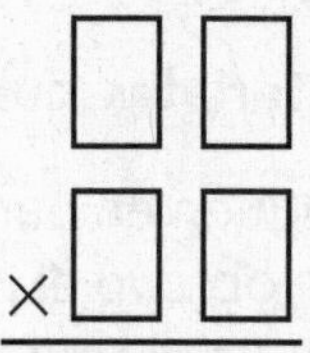

Observe Your Child

If your child gets an incorrect answer, help him or her find the error in his or her computation.

Nombre ______________________________

De la escuela al hogar (en español)
Tema **4**

Usar estrategias y propiedades para multiplicar por números de 2 dígitos

Estimada familia:

Su niño(a) está aprendiendo a multiplicar números de 2 dígitos por números de 2 dígitos. Algunas estrategias que él o ella está aprendiendo incluyen matrices y productos parciales. Debajo hay ejemplos para 13×25.

Usar una matriz.
Sumar cada parte de la matriz para hallar el producto.

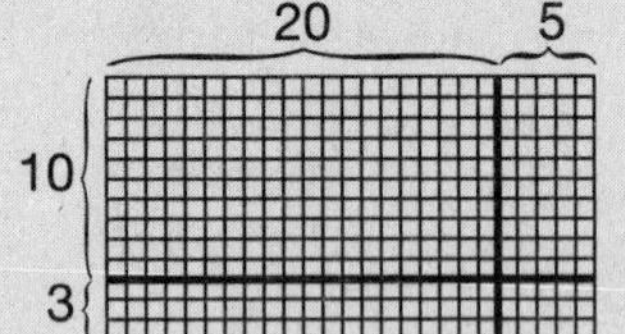

$10 \times 20 = 200$
$10 \times 5 = 50$
$3 \times 20 = 60$
$3 \times 5 = 15$
325

Usar matrices y productos parciales.
Multiplicar las unidades y, luego, las decenas.
Sumar los productos parciales.

$$\begin{array}{r} 25 \\ \times\ 13 \\ \hline 15 \\ 60 \\ 50 \\ +\ 200 \\ \hline 325 \end{array}$$

15, 60: Multiplicar las unidades.
50, 200: Multiplicar las decenas.
325: Sumar los productos parciales.

Jugar a multiplicar

Materiales cubo numérico (rotulado 1 a 6)

Jueguen en parejas. Cada jugador lanza el cubo numérico. Anoten el número que obtuvo el primer jugador en la posición de las decenas y el número que obtuvo el segundo jugador en la posición de las unidades para crear un número de 2 dígitos. Cada jugador lanza el cubo numérico otra vez y anota los números de la misma manera. Luego, los jugadores resuelven la multiplicación. Cuando un jugador halla la respuesta, él o ella dice "Listo". El otro jugador comprueba la respuesta. Si es correcta, él o ella recibe un punto. El primer jugador en acumular 3 puntos gana el juego.

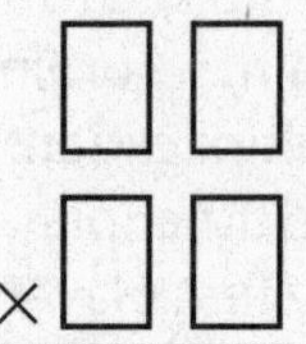

Observe a su niño(a)

Si su niño(a) obtiene una respuesta incorrecta, ayúdelo(a) a hallar el error en su cálculo.

Name ______________________________

Pick a Project

Project 4A

Sabal Palms

The sabal palm, also known as the sabal palmetto, has been the official tree of the state of South Carolina since the Revolutionary War. Sabal palms thrive in hot, humid weather and can survive drought conditions, needing less water than other species of trees. The bud of a sabal palm, known as heart of palm, can be eaten.

An image of a sabal palm can be seen on the South Carolina state seal.

Your Project Explain the Processes

Have students research how tall the sabal palm can grow in meters. Imagine that you stacked 12 sabal palms on top of each other. What would be the combined height of the 12 sabal palms? Estimate the answer to the problem, and then solve the problem in 2 different ways. Present your work to the class. Show the steps you used to estimate the answer, and then demonstrate the 2 ways you solved the answer.

Name ____________________

Pick a Project

Project 4B

Northern Mockingbird

Northern mockingbirds are the only type of mockingbird typically found in North America, specifically in Florida and Texas. The scientific name for this mockingbird is *Mimus polyglottos*, which means "many-tongued mimic" in Latin. It refers to the bird's ability to imitate many different sounds.

Northern mockingbirds eat both insects and fruit. These birds are usually found on the edges of forests, in grasslands, and some open areas.

Your Project Write a Report About the Northern Mockingbird

Research the northern mockingbird. Find several number facts about the northern mockingbird that you find interesting. Then write a report using the facts to ask and answer questions involving multiplication.

Name ___________________________

Pick a Project

Project 4C

World Cup and Women's World Cup

The World Cup is a men's soccer tournament that is played every 4 years. Thirty-two teams representing countries from around the world compete against each other to win the cup. The first World Cup was played in 1930. There have been 21 World Cup tournaments since then, and as of 2017, Brazil has won more championships than any other country.

The Women's World Cup is a soccer tournament that also is played every 4 years. There are only 24 teams from around the world that compete in the tournament. The first Women's World Cup was played in 1991. There have been 7 Women's World Cup tournaments since then, and as of 2018, the United States has won 3 championships, more than any other country.

Your Project Create an Array Poster

Find the number of starting players on every soccer team and the number of teams that play in the Women's World Cup. Then use an array and partial products to find the total number of players on all of the teams.

Create a poster that shows the array you drew, the partial products you found, and the total number of starting players on the teams in the Women's World Cup. Present your work to the class.

Name ______________________

Pick a Project

Project 4D

Shot Put

The shot put is a track-and-field event in which a shot, a heavy object shaped like a ball, is "put," or thrown with a pushing motion, from a circle on the field. The history of events like the shot put may go back as far as the Middle Ages, when soldiers competed to see how far they could throw cannonballs. The shot put has been part of the Olympics since 1896 for men and since 1948 for women. The mass of a shot for a male in competition is 7.26 kilograms (or 16 pounds). The mass of a shot for a woman competing is 4 kilograms (or 8 pounds).

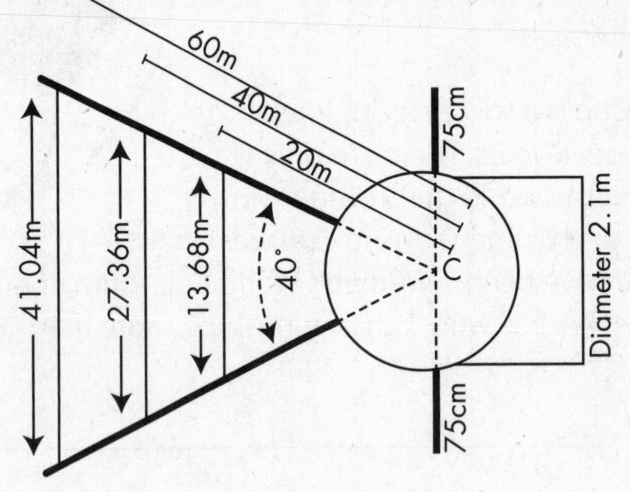

Your Project: Compare Shot Masses

Balls used in different sports vary in weight. For example, the mass of a table tennis ball is about 3 grams, and the mass of a volleyball is about 280 grams. That is nearly 100 times heavier than the table tennis ball!

Research the mass of the balls used in some of your favorite sports. Record the masses in whole grams. On a poster display the masses you researched and display them in a table. Write 3–5 multiplication statements to compare the masses.

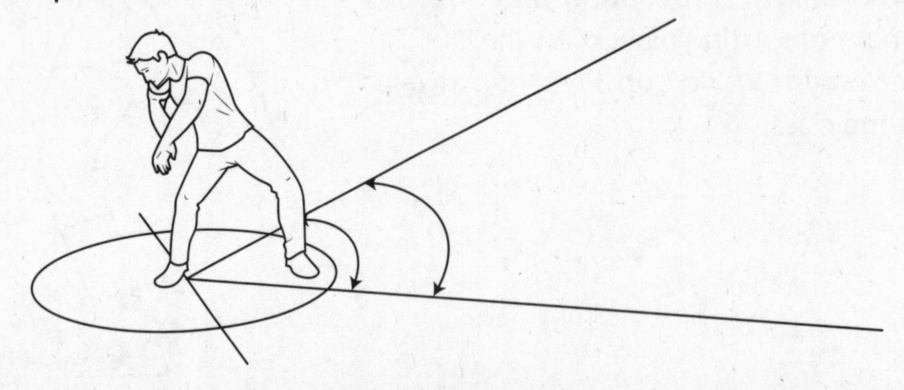

Name ____________________

Planning a Wind Farm

Did You Know? A large wind turbine can produce more than one megawatt of electricity. 1 megawatt is the same as 1,000,000 watts. This is enough electricity to light ten thousand 100-watt light bulbs.

A wind farm has many wind turbines often arranged in arrays. Some wind farms produce enough electricity for thousands of households.

A city of about 200,000 people is planning to build a wind farm. They want the wind farm to generate enough electricity for the entire city. The city estimates that they need at least 6,750 megawatts per hour of electricity.

Use the information in the table to decide which plan the city should choose.

Plan	Wind Farm Array	Megawatts per Turbine per Hour	Total Number of Turbines	Total Megawatts per Hour
A	43 rows of 20	8		
B	19 rows of 50	7		
C	28 rows of 40	6		
D	33 rows of 30	7		

1. Complete the table.

2. **Extension** Which plan should the city choose? Explain.

____

____

____

Name ____________________

enVision® STEM
Activity
4-6

Fossil Fuels

Did You Know? Coal, petroleum (oil), and natural gas are fossil fuels. These fuel sources are formed when buried dead plants and animals decompose. This takes thousands and thousands of years. Because this process takes so long, these fuels are called *nonrenewable* fuel sources. According to the Department of Energy, 85% of the total energy production in the U.S. comes from fossil fuels.

Coal, petroleum, and natural gas can be used to create electricity. The amount of electricity used can be measured in kilowatt-hours (kWh).

1. The table below shows the daily usage of electricity in households in several states. Complete the table by finding the amount of electricity used in one, four, and six weeks.

State	Average Daily Usage (kWh)	Average Weekly Usage (kWh)	Average 4-Week Usage (kWh)	Average 6-Week Usage (kWh)
Massachusetts	21			
Illinois	26			
Florida	37			
Texas	41			
California	19			

2. Find the difference between the least and greatest average 6-week usage.

____

3. Factors such as climate, lifestyle, and family size affect usage rates. Consumers in year-round temperate climates use less electricity for heating and cooling. Which state has the least average usage? What factors might influence that state's electric usage?

____

____

____

4. **Extension** One gallon of oil produces about 15 kilowatt-hours of electricity. About how many gallons of oil would it take for a household's daily consumption of electricity in Illinois?

____

Name ____________________

Daily Review

4-1

1. Voula collected shells on the beach during her summer vacation. If she collected 10 shells each day of her 5-day vacation, how many shells did Voula collect in all?

Ⓐ 15 shells

Ⓑ 30 shells

Ⓒ 50 shells

Ⓓ 60 shells

2. Susana has $30. She plans to buy a game that costs $16 and a game that costs $11. How much money will Susana have left over?

Ⓐ $27

Ⓑ $26

Ⓒ $4

Ⓓ $3

3. Mr. Horn separated the band into 4 equal groups. There are 36 members in each group. Which shows how many students are in the band?

Ⓐ $36 + 4$

Ⓑ $36 - 4$

Ⓒ $36 \div 4$

Ⓓ 36×4

4. Which shows four thousand, seven hundred twenty-nine using base-ten numerals?

Ⓐ 47,029

Ⓑ 7,429

Ⓒ 4,729

Ⓓ 4,029

5. Write a multiplication equation that describes the array shown below.

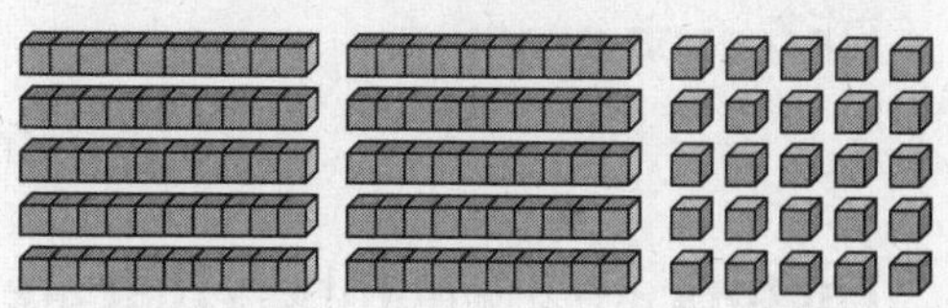

____

6. The distance from Michael's house to his grandmother's house is 84 miles round trip. If Michael visits his grandmother 9 times each year, how many miles does he travel to and from his grandmother's each year?

____

7. The product of two factors is 490. One factor is 7. What is the other factor? Use a basic multiplication fact and place value to explain your reasoning.

____

____

____

____

____

Name ______________________

Reteach to Build Understanding
4-1

Vocabulary

1. A **product** is an answer to a multiplication problem.

Find each product.

$3 \times 8 =$ ______ $7 \times 6 =$ ______ $2 \times 5 =$ ______

2. **Factors** are the numbers that are multiplied together to give a product.

Find each missing factor.

$9 \times$ ______ $= 54$ ______ $\times 4 = 12$ ______ $\times 6 = 30$

Each of the multiplication sentences above is an example of a basic fact. You can use basic facts and place value to multiply multiples of 10.

Remember that ten tens or ten × ten equals one hundred.

3. 3 × 6 = 18 ← Basic fact

30 × **60** = 1,8**00**

↑ ↑ ↑

3 tens × ______ tens = 18 hundreds

4. 4 × 5 = 20 ← Basic fact

40 × **50** = 2,0**00**

↑ ↑ ↑

______ tens × ______ tens = ______________________

Use a basic fact and place value to multiply.

5. $6 \times 7 = 42$

$60 \times 7 =$ ______

$60 \times 70 =$ ______

6. $8 \times 9 =$ ______

$80 \times 9 =$ ______

$80 \times 90 =$ ______

On the Back!

7. Use basic facts and place value to find 30×30.

Name ___________________________

Read the problem below. Select the answer to each question.

Reasoning The product of two factors is 4,200. If one of the factors is 60, what is the other factor? Explain.

1. Which equation represents the statement "The product of two factors is 4,200."?

Ⓐ factor + factor = 4,200

Ⓑ factor − factor = 4,200

Ⓒ factor × factor = 4,200

Ⓓ factor ÷ factor = 4,200

2. What does the number 60 represent in the problem?

Ⓐ The product of two factors

Ⓑ The known factor

Ⓒ The unknown factor

Ⓓ Both factors

3. Using estimation, which of the following is closest in value to the unknown factor?

Ⓐ 1

Ⓑ 10

Ⓒ 100

Ⓓ 1,000

4. Explain a strategy that would help you solve this problem.

____

____

____

Name ______________________

Enrichment

4-1

Multiply to Solve

1. The Parent Association (PA) is ordering caramel apples. A box holds 20 caramel apples. If the PA ordered 50 boxes, how many caramel apples did they order? Show your work.

____

2. Paul needs to explain to his class how to use mental math to find the product of 40×50. What should Paul tell his class?

____

____

____

____

3. Maggie meditates 10 minutes each day before school and 30 minutes each day after school. She attends school Monday through Friday. How many minutes does Maggie meditate in 4 weeks? Show your work.

____

____

4. Mrs. Teagan is collecting dimes from her family members. Each of her 5 family members gave her 8 dimes at the end of the week. How much money did Mrs. Teagan have at the end of the week? Show your work.

____

5. Nick volunteers at the senior center each Saturday for 60 minutes and each Sunday for 40 minutes. He takes two weeks off for vacation each year. How many minutes does Nick volunteer in one year? Show your work.

____

____

Name ____________________

Daily Review
4-2

1. Mrs. Jackson has 806 marigold seeds. How many marigold seeds does she have rounded to the nearest ten?

Ⓐ 800 marigold seeds
Ⓑ 805 marigold seeds
Ⓒ 810 marigold seeds
Ⓓ 900 marigold seeds

2. Harvey can read 17 pages in one hour. In one week, he spent 6 hours reading. How many pages did Harvey read that week?

Ⓐ 102 pages
Ⓑ 42 pages
Ⓒ 23 pages
Ⓓ 11 pages

3. Tyler mows 7 lawns every week. He earns $10 for mowing each lawn. How much will he earn in 6 weeks?

Ⓐ $42
Ⓑ $60
Ⓒ $70
Ⓓ $420

4. Which shows 22,211? Select all that apply.

☐ twenty-two thousand, two hundred eleven
☐ 20,000 + 2,000 + 200 + 10 + 1
☐ twenty-two thousand, eleven
☐ 2,000 + 200 + 11
☐ 22 hundreds two hundred 11

5. A hardware store has 1,056 boxes of long nails and 502 boxes of short nails. How many more boxes of long nails are there than boxes of short nails?

____

6. Wendell bought a box of 213 craft sticks. He used some craft sticks to make two model houses. He has 99 craft sticks left. How many craft sticks did Wendell use?

____

7. Charles works 40 hours every week. How many hours will he work in 50 weeks? Use a basic fact and place value to explain how to solve the problem.

____
____
____
____
____

8. Compare 37,007 and 30,707. Which is greater?

____

Name ______________________________

Vocabulary

1. An **array** is a model used to display objects in rows and columns. This place-value block array models 10 groups of 14.

   There are ______ groups of 10.

   There are ______ groups of 4.

2. **Partial products** are products found by breaking one factor into ones, tens, hundreds, and so on and then multiplying each of these by the other factor.

   Find the product of 10×14.

   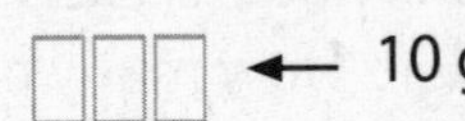
   ← 10 groups of 10 or $10 \times 10 = 100$.

   ← 10 groups of 4 or $10 \times 4 = 40$.

   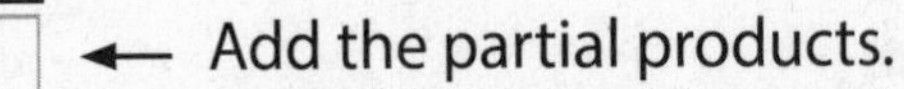
   ← Add the partial products.

Use the array at the right to find the product of 20×15.

3. There are ______ groups of 10.

   There are ______ groups of ______.

   Find the partial products.

   $20 \times 10 =$ ______ $20 \times$ ______ $=$ ______

   Add the partial products.

   ______ + ______ = ______

   So, $20 \times 15 =$ ______.

4. Draw an array to find the product of 30×26.

   30 groups of 20 = ______ 30 groups of 6 = ______

   ______ + ______ = ______

   So, $30 \times 26 =$ ______.

On the Back!

5. Draw an array to find the product of 40×21.

Name ______________________

Build Mathematical Literacy
4-2

Read the problem. Answer the questions to help understand the problem.

Algebra In the first 3 months of the year, an electronics store sold 1,446 cameras. How many cameras did the store sell in March? Write and solve an equation.

DATA

Camera Sales	
Month	**Number Sold**
January	486
February	385

Interpret the table for 1–3.

1. What data does the first column of the table provide?

____

2. What data does the second column of the table provide?

____

3. If another row was added to the table, what would you expect it to show?

____

____

Use the data in the table for 4.

4. How many cameras have been sold in the months shown?

____

5. How many cameras were sold in January, February, and March?

____

6. Why isn't the answer to Exercise 4 the same as the answer to Exercise 5? How does this help you solve the problem?

____

____

____

____

Name ____________________

Enrichment
4-2

A Finished Product!

Find each partial product. Then, use numbers from the equations to complete the sentences.

1. $30 \times 20 =$ ________ Marie had ________ songs on her music player.

$30 \times 4 =$ ________ She added ________ more songs.

$30 \times 24 =$ ________ Now Marie has a total of ________ songs.

2. $60 \times 80 =$ ________ A sporting goods manufacturer shipped out ________

$60 \times 3 =$ ________ bowling pins and ________ bowling balls to an

$60 \times 83 =$ ________ alley. There were ________ items in all.

3. $90 \times 70 =$ ________ The population of Desertvale was recorded at

$90 \times 4 =$ ________ ________ in January. There were ________ more

$90 \times 74 =$ ________ people added in a year. The following January,

the population of Desertvale was ________.

4. $80 \times 80 =$ ________ Jed estimated that there were ________

$80 \times 5 =$ ________ jellybeans in a jar. When the jellybeans were finally

$80 \times 85 =$ ________ counted, Jed found there were actually ________

more. In fact, there were ________ jellybeans in all.

5. $40 \times 50 =$ ________ Now, create your own sentences using the equations in Exercise **5**.

$40 \times 2 =$ ________

____

$40 \times 52 =$ ________

Name ______________________

Daily Review
4-3

1. Why is 4,532 less than 4,541?

   Ⓐ It has fewer ones.
   Ⓑ It has fewer tens.
   Ⓒ It has fewer hundreds.
   Ⓓ It has fewer thousands.

2. The table below shows how many magazines four schools sold for a fundraiser. Which school sold the least number of magazines?

School	Magazines Sold
Lane School	1,569
Jefferson School	1,539
Smith School	1,505
Lincoln School	1,560

   Ⓐ Lane School
   Ⓑ Jefferson School
   Ⓒ Smith School
   Ⓓ Lincoln School

3. Last year, 288 people saw the school play. This year, 91 more people saw the play. What is the best estimate of how many people saw the play this year?

   Ⓐ About 300 people
   Ⓑ About 400 people
   Ⓒ About 500 people
   Ⓓ About 600 people

4. Rick makes 50 picture frames each week. How many frames does he make in 20 weeks?

____

5. Kurt has 316 books. Jenna has 321 books. Dale has 99 books. How many books do they have in all?

____

6. Mr. Silva has 8 boxes of drills at his store. Each box has 24 drills. How many drills does Mr. Silva have? Explain how you found your answer.

____

____

____

____

____

____

____

____

7. What is 30×60?

____

Name ______________________________

Reteach to Build Understanding
4-3

Vocabulary

1. **Compatible numbers** are numbers that are easy to compute mentally. You can use compatible numbers to estimate.

   Use compatible numbers to estimate 26×31.
   26 is close to 25, and 31 is close to 30.

   So, 26×31 is about 25×30.

   Remember to look for multiplication patterns.

   $25 \times 3 =$ ______, so $25 \times 30 =$ ______.

   26×31 is about ______.

2. Use compatible numbers to estimate 27×42.

   Find compatible numbers.

   27 is close to ______.

   42 is close to 40.

   Use number patterns to multiply the compatible numbers.

   ______ $\times 4 =$ ______

   ______ $\times 40 =$ __________

   27×42 is about __________.

3. Use compatible numbers to estimate 46×68.

   46 is close to ______.

   68 is close to ______.

   46×68 is about ______ $\times$ ______ $=$ __________.

4. 79×12 is about ______ $\times$ ______ $=$ ______.

5. 95×11 is about ______ $\times$ ______ $=$ ______.

On the Back!

6. Use compatible numbers to estimate 27×19.

Name ______________________________

Read the problem. Complete the Frayer Models to help understand the terms used in the problem.

Higher Order Thinking How is using compatible numbers to estimate like rounding? How is it different?

Definition	**Characteristic**
compatible numbers	
Examples	**Non-Examples**

Definition	**Characteristic**
rounding	
Examples	**Non-Examples**

Name ______________________

Approximate Eggs

Molly lives on a farm. Her family sells eggs in cartons holding 24 or 48 eggs. Explain how to use compatible numbers to estimate each of the following.

1. About how many eggs are in 38 of the small cartons?

2. In March, Molly's family sold 82 of the small cartons and 29 of the large cartons. About how many eggs did they sell in all?

3. In April, Molly's family sold 21 of the large cartons and three times as many small cartons. About how many eggs did they sell in all?

4. In May, Molly's family sold 19 of the large cartons and 32 more small cartons than large cartons. About how many more eggs did they sell in small cartons than in large ones?

Name ______________________

Daily Review

4-4

1. Nola earns $62 each week walking dogs. About how much money does Nola make in 52 weeks?

Ⓐ $3,000
Ⓑ $300
Ⓒ $110
Ⓓ $10

2. Seven students are planning to take an exercise class. If the cost is $12 for each student, how much will it cost for all 7 students to take one class?

Ⓐ $80
Ⓑ $82
Ⓒ $84
Ⓓ $86

3. Which expressions can be used to find the product 6,300? Select all that apply.

☐ 7×900
☐ $(7 \times 9) + (10 \times 10)$
☐ 700×9
☐ $(63) + (100)$
☐ 70×90

4. What is the sum of 12,678 and 409,107?

Ⓐ 401,785
Ⓑ 420,705
Ⓒ 420,780
Ⓓ 421,785

5. Kelly is buying 2 front-row tickets for $35 each and 2 bleacher tickets for $15 each. How much money will Kelly spend on the tickets?

____

6. What is 4,875 rounded to the nearest hundred?

____

7. A company needs to buy 4 computers. Each computer costs $1,395. How much will the company spend on all 4 computers?

____

8. A news article reported that about 9,000 people attended a local festival. The actual number of people was 8,735 people. How much greater is the estimate than the actual number of people?

____

9. Write 217,418 in expanded form.

____

____

____

Name ______________________

Vocabulary

1. An **array** is a model used to display objects in rows and columns. You can use an array to find the product of two 2-digit numbers.

   The array at the right represents 14×18. Draw lines through the array to show the tens and ones in each factor.

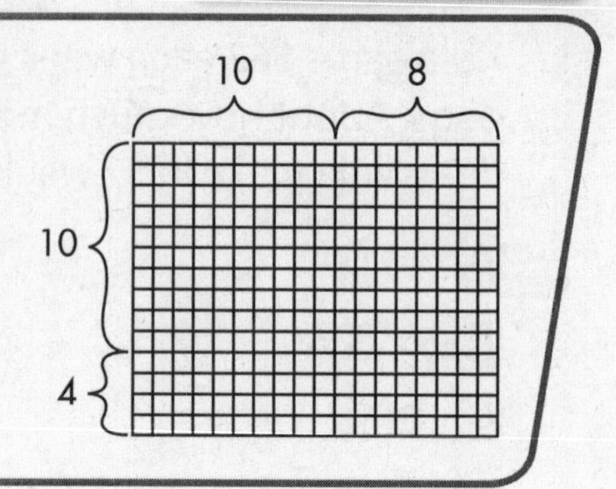

2. Use the array for 14×18 to find each partial product.

   $10 \times 10 =$ ______

   $10 \times 8 =$ ______

   $4 \times 10 =$ ______

   $4 \times 8 =$ ______

   Add the partial products to find the product of 14×18.

   ______ + ______ + ______ + ______ = ______

   So, $14 \times 18 =$ ______.

3. What two factors are shown by the array at the right?

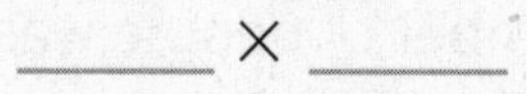

   ______ × ______

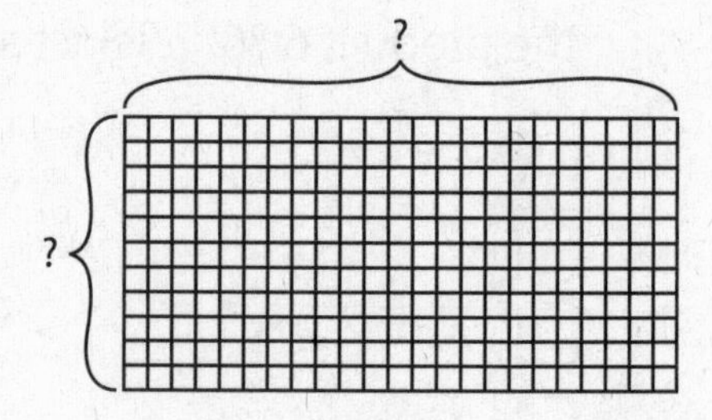

   Draw lines through the array to show the tens and ones in each factor.

   Find each partial product, and then add to find the product. ______ × ______ = ______

4. Draw an array to find the product of 17×17.

   $17 \times 17 =$ ______

On the Back!

5. Draw an array to find the product of 12×27.

Name ______________________________

Build Mathematical Literacy
4-4

Read the problem. Answer the questions to help understand how to solve the problem.

The flagpole in front of City Hall in Lou's town is 35 feet tall. How many inches tall is the flagpole? Remember, there are 12 inches in 1 foot.

K What do you **KNOW** from the information stated in the problem?	
N What information do you **NOT** need to know to solve the problem?	
W **WHAT** exactly does the problem want you to find?	
S What **STRATEGY** or operation will I use to solve this problem?	

CHECK: How does knowing the relationship between feet and inches help you know that your answer is reasonable?

____

____

Name ______________________________

Food for Thought

You work at a pet shop. One of your jobs is to feed all the animals. Answer the questions below using the chart at the right.

Daily Feeding Chart

Fish	11 super pellets each or 32 mini pellets each
Puppies	16 oz dry food each or 12 oz wet food each

First thing in the morning you feed the fish. The 12 fish tanks have a total of 26 large fish. You can choose between two kinds of pellets.

1. Which kind of pellets do you choose? Estimate the number of pellets you need. Explain your method.

____

____

____

2. What is the exact number of pellets?

____

You feed the puppies next. There are 10 cages of large-breed puppies. Each cage can hold 3 puppies, but 2 of the cages only have 2 puppies each. You need to decide which food to give the puppies.

3. What kind of puppy food do you choose? Estimate the amount of puppy food you need. Explain your method.

____

____

____

4. What is the exact amount of puppy food?

____

____

Name ______________________

Daily Review

4-5

Carla is keeping track of the number of tomatoes that she sets out on her table at the Farmer's Market. The table below shows the number of tomatoes that she has set out each day this week.

Tomatoes for Sale

Day	Number of Tomatoes
Monday	26
Tuesday	49
Wednesday	34
Thursday	59
Friday	17

For Exercises **1** and **2**, use the table.

1. Which is the best estimate for the total number of tomatoes that Carla has set out this week?

Ⓐ 150 tomatoes

Ⓑ 170 tomatoes

Ⓒ 190 tomatoes

Ⓓ 200 tomatoes

2. The total number of tomatoes that Carla has displayed this month is 4 times the number she set out on Wednesday and Thursday combined. How many tomatoes has she displayed this month?

Ⓐ 480 tomatoes

Ⓑ 372 tomatoes

Ⓒ 362 tomatoes

Ⓓ 93 tomatoes

3. Coal City has a population of 24,902 people. Iron City has a population of 24,859 people. Use the symbols $>$ or $<$ to write a comparison of the two populations.

____

____

4. Ted has 40 pigs in each pigpen on his farm. He has 4 pens. How many pigs does Ted have in all of the pens?

____

5. Jorge went to the store with $200. He bought a sweatshirt for $22 and shoes for $27. How much money did he have left after his purchases? Explain.

____

____

____

____

____

____

6. What is the value of the 4 in 24,659?

____

Name ______________________

Reteach to Build Understanding
4-5

Vocabulary

1. The **Distributive Property** states that multiplying a sum by a number is the same as multiplying each number in the sum by that number and adding the products.

   Rewrite 36×15 using the Distributive Property.

   $36 \times 15 = (30 + 6) \times (10 + 5)$

   $= (30 + 6) \times 10 + (30 + 6) \times 5$

   $= (30 \times \_\_\_\_) + (6 \times \_\_\_\_) + (30 \times \_\_\_\_) + (6 \times \_\_\_\_)$

2. Use the area model and the Distributive Property to find 24×19.

	10	9
20	20 × 10	20 × 9
4	4 × 10	4 × 9

   Break apart 24 and 19.

   $24 \times 19 = (\_\_\_\_ + 4) \times (\_\_\_\_ + 9)$

   Multiply (20 + 4) by 10. Multiply (20 + 4) by 9.

   $= (20 + 4) \times \_\_\_\_ + (20 + 4) \times \_\_\_\_$

   Distribute both the 10 and the 9.

   $= (20 \times \_\_\_\_) + (4 \times \_\_\_\_) + (20 \times \_\_\_\_) + (4 \times \_\_\_\_)$

   $= \_\_\_\_ + \_\_\_\_ + \_\_\_\_ + \_\_\_\_$

   $= \_\_\_\_$

3. Draw an area model and use the Distributive Property to find 32×21.

   $32 \times 21 = \_\_\_\_$

4. Use the Distributive Property to find 19×19.

   $19 \times 19 = \_\_\_\_$

On the Back!

5. Draw an area model and use the Distributive Property to find 13×28.

Name ___________________________________

Read the problem below. Then circle True or False for each statement. For each statement that is false, explain why using details from the text.

Marla wants to buy a new tablet that costs $565, including tax. She saved $15 per week for 30 weeks. Does Marla have enough money saved to buy the tablet? Explain.

1. The total cost of the tablet will be more than $565 after tax is added. True False

2. Marla can't buy the tablet because she only saved $15. True False

3. You can use the expression 15×30 to find the total amount of money that Marla saved. True False

4. Marla needs to save at least $565 to buy the tablet. True False

5. The total amount of money Marla saved is the final answer to the problem. True False

Name ___________________________

Enrichment
4-5

Jackson's Bakery

$15 FRUIT TART
$18 MUDSLIDE PIE
$22 CHEESECAKE
$27 ICE CREAM CAKE

1. Jackson's Bakery sold 29 cheesecakes in one day. How much money did Jackson's Bakery make in one day from cheesecakes?

____

2. Jackson's Bakery sold 15 ice cream cakes and 31 fruit tarts in one weekend. How much money did Jackson's Bakery make in one weekend from ice cream cakes and fruit tarts?

____

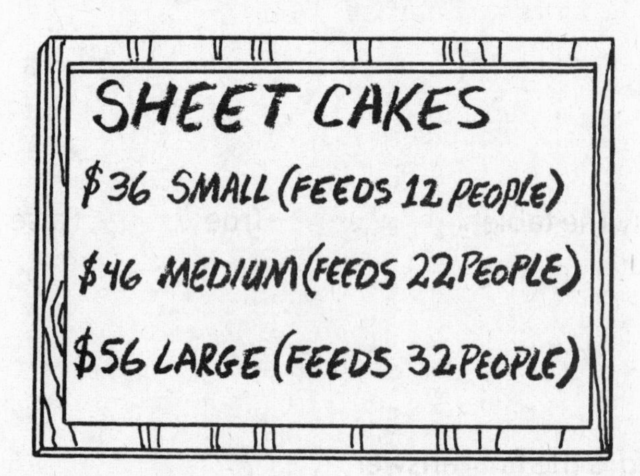

SHEET CAKES
$36 SMALL (FEEDS 12 PEOPLE)
$46 MEDIUM (FEEDS 22 PEOPLE)
$56 LARGE (FEEDS 32 PEOPLE)

3. The new pastry chef at Jackson's Bakery specializes in sheet cakes for parties. She sold 17 small, 11 medium, and 20 large sheet cakes in one week. How much money did Jackson's Bakery make in one week from sheet cakes?

____

4. How many people would all of the sheet cakes sold in problem 3 feed?

____

Name ______________________________

Daily Review

4-6

1. In which number is the value of the ten thousands digit 10 times as great as the value of the thousands digit?

Ⓐ 212,260

Ⓑ 221,370

Ⓒ 233,410

Ⓓ 234,420

2. The cost of a hotel room is $135 per night. How much will it cost to stay at the hotel for 6 nights?

Ⓐ $690

Ⓑ $720

Ⓒ $810

Ⓓ $980

3. Which is the best estimate for 53×82?

Ⓐ 400

Ⓑ 4,000

Ⓒ 40,000

Ⓓ 45,000

4. Which of the following expressions shows a way to use mental math to find the product of 7×38? Select all that apply.

☐ $(7 \times 30) + (7 \times 8)$

☐ $(7 \times 30 \times 8)$

☐ $(7 \times 40) - (7 \times 2)$

☐ $(7 \times 3) + (7 \times 8)$

☐ $(5 \times 30) + (2 \times 8)$

5. On Saturday, 24,156 people visited the zoo. On Sunday, 22,498 people visited the zoo. How many more people went to the zoo on Saturday than on Sunday?

____

6. A company ordered shirts for all of its employees to wear at the company picnic. The table shows how many shirts of each size were ordered. Each shirt costs $12. Estimate how much money the company spent on the shirts. Show your work.

Shirt Size	Number of Shirts
Small	16
Medium	22
Large	24

____

____

____

7. Paul says 3×600 has the same value as 6×300. Is Paul correct? Explain.

____

____

____

____

____

Name ______________________________

Vocabulary

1. **Partial products** are products found by multiplying each place value of both factors.

   This area model shows

   ______ × ______.

   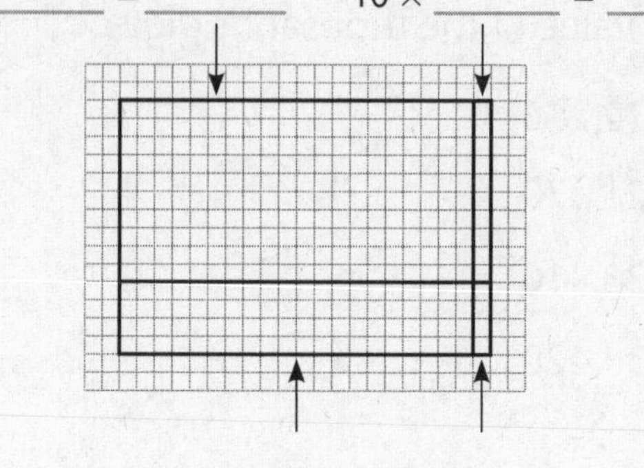

   Each area represents a different partial product. Complete each equation.

   What are the partial products?

   ____

2. The area model shows 15 × 22.

   What are the partial products?

   ____

   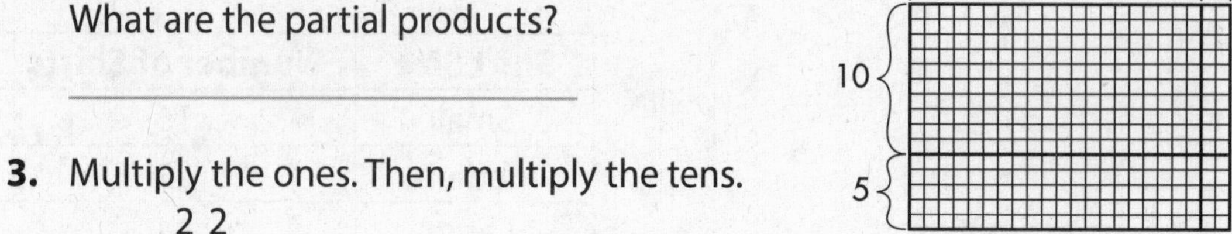

3. Multiply the ones. Then, multiply the tens.

```
      2 2
  ×   1 5
  -------
      ☐☐   ← What is 5 × 2?
    ☐☐☐   ← What is 5 × 20?
      ☐☐   ← What is 10 × 2?
  + ☐☐☐   ← What is 10 × 20?
  -------
    ☐☐☐   ← Add the partial products.
```

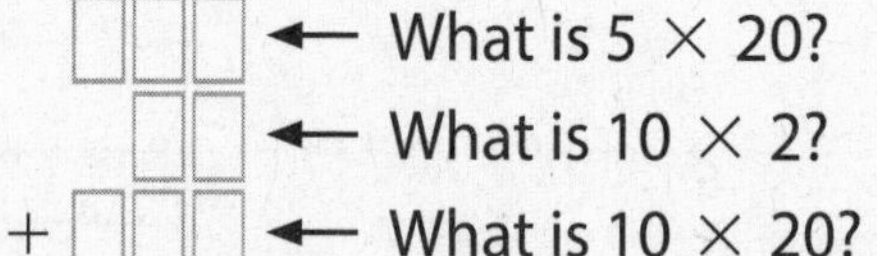

4.

```
      1 2
  ×   1 4
  -------
       ☐   ← What is ______ × 2?
      ☐☐   ← What is 4 × ______?
      ☐☐   ← What is ______ × ______?
  + ☐☐☐   ← What is ______ × ______?
  -------
    ☐☐☐   ← Add the partial products.
```

On the Back!

5. Draw an area model for 13 × 18. Use your area model to find the partial products and solve.

Name ____________________

Build Mathematical Literacy
4-6

Read the problem. Answer the questions to help you draw a picture that represents the problem.

Construct Arguments A school has 2 large patios. One is rectangular and is 24 feet long by 18 feet wide. The other is square and each side is 21 feet long. Which patio has a greater area? Explain.

1. Underline the number of patios that you should draw to represent the problem.
2. Circle the shapes of the patios that you should draw to represent the problem.
3. Draw boxes around the dimensions of the patios.
4. Why does one patio have only one measurement given?

 ____

 ____

5. Draw and label the patios.

6. Describe the part of your drawing that represents the area of each patio.

 ____

 ____

7. Can you use the drawings without the measurements to determine which patio has a greater area? Explain.

 ____

 ____

 ____

Name ____________________

Ticket Reasoning

A New York theater company is putting on a play in Kaytown. Some local fifth-grade students are selling tickets to raise money for a class-field trip. The class gets $18 for each ticket the students sell.

Use the following clues and answer the questions to find how much money the students make. Show all your partial products when you multiply two-digit numbers.

- Kara sold twelve times as many tickets as Max.
- Max sold 28 fewer tickets than Manny.
- Manny sold 15 times as many tickets as Kalinda.
- Kalinda sold 3 tickets.

1. How many tickets did each student sell? Explain your reasoning.

2. How much money did Manny make?

Name ______________________

State parks are popular places to visit. The table below shows how many people visited a state park in four different years.

Year	Number of Visitors
2012	40,648
2013	81,355
2014	33,837
2015	54,022

For Exercises **1** and **2**, use the table.

1. What is the difference between the greatest and the least number of visitors?

Ⓐ 27,333 visitors
Ⓑ 40,687 visitors
Ⓒ 47,518 visitors
Ⓓ 52,522 visitors

2. How many visitors did the state park have from 2012 to 2015 in all?

Ⓐ 40,648 visitors
Ⓑ 122,003 visitors
Ⓒ 155,840 visitors
Ⓓ 209,862 visitors

3. The first Ferris wheel was a hit at the 1893 Chicago World's Fair. Each of its 36 cars carried 40 riders. How many riders could fill 20 cars?

Ⓐ 80 riders
Ⓑ 600 riders
Ⓒ 800 riders
Ⓓ 8,000 riders

4. One fourth-grade class ate 32 slices of pizza for lunch. Each of the 6 fourth-grade classes ate the same amount of pizza. How many slices of pizza did the fourth graders eat in all?

____

5. A roller coaster has a train of 5 cars. Each car can hold a maximum of 4 people. In one hour, the roller coaster train runs 12 times. What is the maximum number of people the roller coaster can hold in one hour?

____

6. Use the area model and the Distributive Property to find 14×27. Find each partial product, and then find the product.

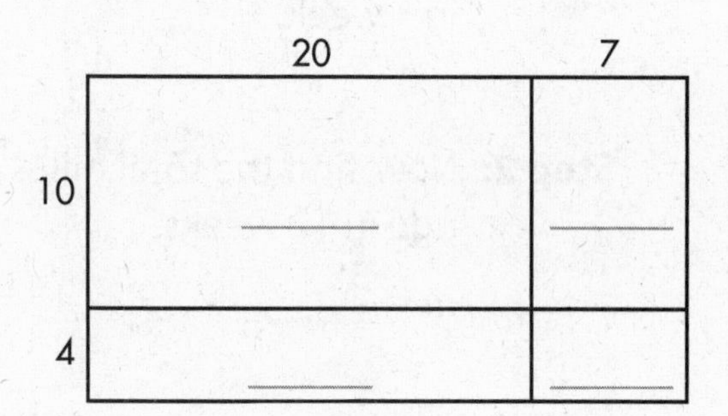

Name ______________________________

Vocabulary

1. A **variable** is a symbol or letter that stands for a number.

Jimmy practices playing the piano for 30 minutes each day, 30 days each month. How many minutes does Jimmy practice playing the piano in one month?

Complete the bar diagram.

Write a multiplication equation for the bar diagram. Let p represent the number of minutes Jimmy practices each month.

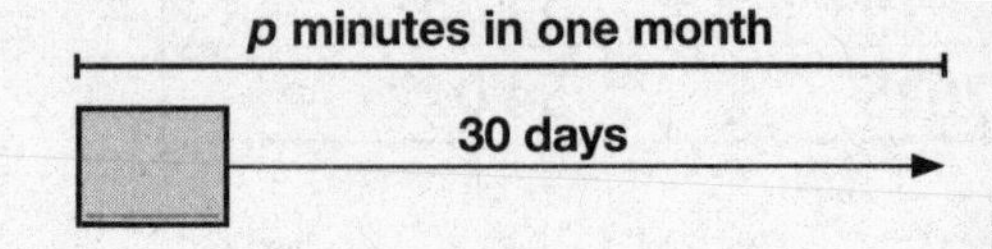

$p = 30 \times$ ______

$p =$ ______

Jimmy practices playing piano ______ minutes in one month.

Margie is training for a bike race. She rides her bike 12 miles every day. If there are 12 weeks until the race, how many miles will Margie ride before the race?

2. Make a plan to solve the problem.

Step 1: First, use a bar diagram to help find the number of miles Margie rides in 1 week.

$d =$ ______ $\times$ ______ $=$ ______

Step 2: Now, find the total miles Margie will ride in 12 weeks.

$m =$ ______ $\times$ ______ $=$ ______

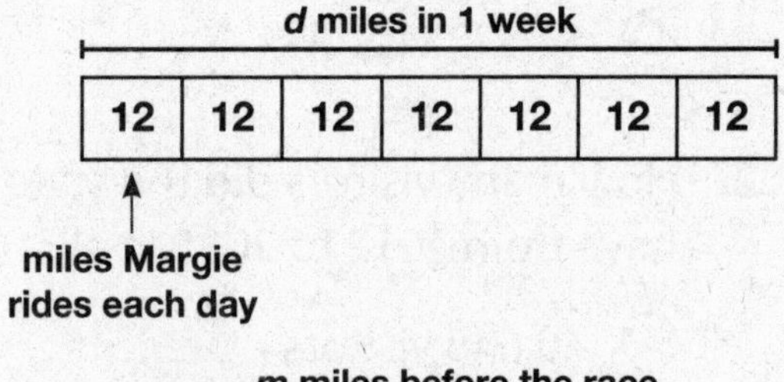

Margie will ride __________ miles before the race.

3. Cami performs 18 back handsprings during a routine. If she practices the routine 13 times, how many back handsprings does Cami perform? Draw a bar diagram and write an equation to solve.

On the Back!

4. Yuri made 12 fruit bouquets as gifts. Each bouquet used 5 oranges, 4 apples, and 2 bananas. How many pieces of fruit did Yuri use to make all 12 fruit bouquets?

Name ______________________________

Build Mathematical Literacy
4-7

Read the problem. Answer the questions to help you understand the problem.

Make Sense and Persevere Jarrod delivers 63 newspapers each Monday through Saturday and 78 newspapers each Sunday. Last month consisted of 4 Sundays and 26 other days. How many newspapers did Jarrod deliver last month?
What strategies can you use to find how many newspapers Jarrod delivered last month?

1. Why is the number of Sundays given separately from the number of other days?

____

____

2. The problem says that last month consisted of 26 other days. Does it matter which days that the other 26 days consist of? Explain.

____

____

3. Jarrod drew a calendar and wrote down the number of papers he delivered each day. He added the numbers together to find the total number of newspapers he delivered. Is this an efficient strategy? Explain.

____

____

4. Write the steps you need to follow to answer the question.

____

____

____

____

____

Name ________________________________

Enrichment
4-7

Which Property?

For questions **1–4,** write the multiplication property that makes the statement true.

1. $7 \times 49 = 49 \times 7$

____

2. $891 \times 0 = 0$

____

3. $1 \times 246 = 246$

____

4. $27 \times 39 = (20 \times 30) + (7 \times 30) + (20 \times 9) + (7 \times 9)$

____

5. How can knowing a multiplication property help you find the product of a problem with three factors, such as $50 \times 86 \times 1$?

____

____

6. If you multiply any number by 1, can the product ever be greater than that number? Explain.

____

____

____

Use multiplication properties to determine the missing number for each box.

7. $2{,}378 \times 5 \times \square = 0$

8. $3 \times (9 \times 17) = (3 \times 9) \times \square$

9. $657 \times \square = 657$

10. $264 \times \square = 39 \times 264$

Name ______________________

Home-School Connection
Topic 5

Use Strategies and Properties to Divide by 1-Digit Numbers

Dear Family,

In this topic, your child will learn how to divide by one-digit divisors. Learning this skill will require his or her understanding of estimating quotients and, of remainders, and of connecting models and symbols. You can expect to see work that provides practice in dividing whole numbers by one-digit divisors using strategies other than the standard algorithm and checking that the answer is reasonable using estimation.

Variations on a Theme

Materials pencil, index cards

Write a ÷ symbol and an = symbol on two index cards. Write the numbers 2 to 9 on separate index cards. Write eight different two-, three-, or four-digit numbers on separate index cards. Place the one-digit and multi-digit cards face down in separate piles. Take turns choosing one card from each pile and using the symbol cards to create a division equation. Take turns solving the problems. If the solution is correct, the person solving the problem earns points equal to the remainder. Take turns until all the cards have been used. The person with the most points wins. Shuffle both stacks of cards and play again.

Observe Your Child

During one of your child's turns, ask your child to explain how to check that the quotient is reasonable.

Nombre ______________________________

De la escuela al hogar
(en español)
Tema **5**

Usar estrategias y propiedades para dividir por números de 1 dígito

Estimada familia:

En este tema, su niño(a) aprenderá a dividir por divisores de un dígito. Aprender esta destreza va a requerir que él o ella entienda cómo estimar cocientes y residuos y cómo conectar modelos y símbolos. Verá trabajo de práctica de división de números enteros por divisores de un dígito usando estrategias distintas del algoritmo convencional y comprobación de respuestas que sean razonables usando la estimación.

Variaciones de un tema

Materiales lápiz, tarjetas de fichero

Escriba un símbolo de ÷ y un símbolo de = en dos tarjetas de fichero. Escriba números del 2 al 9 en distintas tarjetas de fichero. Escriba ocho números de dos, tres o cuatro dígitos en distintas tarjetas de fichero. Coloque boca abajo las tarjetas de un dígito y de varios dígitos en dos pilas distintas. Túrnense para elegir una tarjeta de cada pila y usar las tarjetas con los símbolos para crear una ecuación de división. Túrnense para resolver los problemas. Si la solución es correcta, la persona que resolvió el problema gana la cantidad de puntos que corresponda al residuo. Túrnense hasta que todas las tarjetas se hayan usado. Gana la persona con más puntos. Mezcle las dos pilas de tarjetas y jueguen otra vez.

Observe a su niño(a)

Durante uno de los turnos de su niño(a), pídale que explique cómo comprobar que el cociente es razonable.

Name ______________________________

Gold Coast Railroad Museum

The Gold Coast Railroad Museum is located in Miami and was founded in 1956. The museum is one of three official state railroad museums for the state of Florida. It was named a state railroad museum in 1984.

The Gold Coast Railroad Museum's exhibits include many historic railroad cars, such as the Western Pacific "Silver Crescent," and engines, such as the Florida East Coast "113." One of the museum's most important exhibits is the presidential railcar "Ferdinand Magellan," which was the official presidential railcar from 1943 through 1958.

Your Project Make a Model

Make a model of a train with 3 to 9 railroad cars. Decide how many seats you want the train to have. Then, determine how many people can sit in each railroad car if your train is filled to capacity with passengers. Indicate your results in your model.

Name ___________________________________

Pick a Project

Project 5B

Atlantic Sailfish

The Atlantic sailfish is a popular game fish that is part of the billfish family, which also includes marlin and spearfish. Sailfish are known for two characteristics: a large dorsal (or top) fin and a jaw that looks like a spear. These fish are a metallic blue color with a white belly underneath.

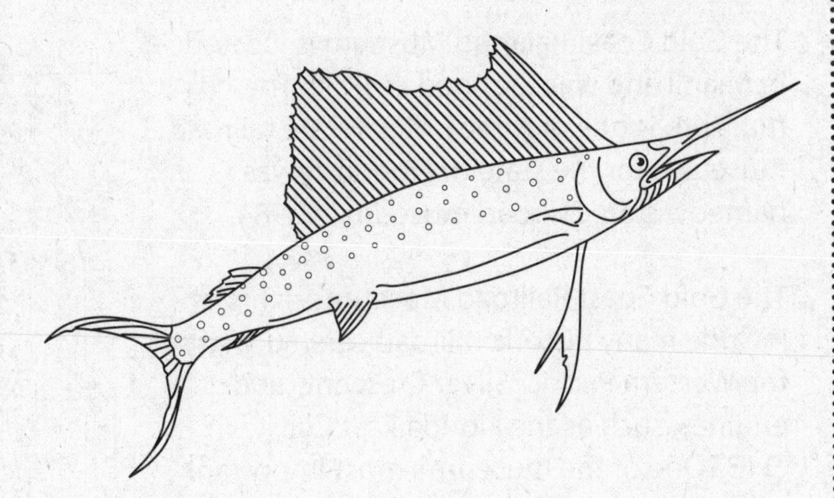

Sailfish are thought to be the fastest fish in the ocean. Some sailfish have been recorded moving at speeds of about 68 miles per hour. But the average speed of a sailfish is between 23 and 34 miles per hour.

Your Project Make a Migration Display

Atlantic Sailfish are abundant in the Gulf of Mexico. Some of these sailfish migrate across the Gulf and travel approximately 896 miles during the months of April and May. How many miles does an Atlantic Sailfish migrate per month? per week? per day?

Create a map display of the Gulf of Mexico. Use or make a map key to summarize the sailfish migration. Share your unique map with the class.

Name ____________________

Pick a Project

Project 5C

Portuguese Water Dog

Portuguese Water Dogs are originally from the coast of Portugal. These dogs were bred to work in the water with fishermen: herding fish into nets, retrieving nets and equipment, and taking messages between ships or between a ship and the shore. For this reason, the American Kennel Club classifies the Portuguese Water Dog as a working dog.

Portuguese Water Dogs have waterproof, nonshedding coats and webbed feet, which help them swim. Portuguese Water Dogs are usually black, brown, or black and brown. They sometimes have white spots.

Your Project Create a Brochure on Portuguese Water Dogs

A breeder has four Portuguese Water Dogs. An adult requires 4 cups of dry food a day. Dry dog food comes in 40-pound and 60-pound bags. A 60-pound bag contains about 240 cups of kibble, and a 40-pound bag contains about 160 cups of kibble. How many days will each bag of kibble last the breeder? How often will the breeder need to buy a 60-pound bag in one month? How many 40-pound bags of kibble will a breeder need to buy in one year?

Create a brochure that will be interesting to a person or family that is thinking about buying a Portuguese Water Dog. Include pictures and information, including some costs involved in owning a Portuguese Water Dog.

Name ______________________________

Electrical Energy

Did You Know? Static electricity occurs in nature. In a thundercloud, tiny bits of ice bump into each other to create an electrical charge. A lightning bolt is a discharge of electricity.

When you plug a lamp or a TV into a wall outlet, you complete an electrical circuit. This is called current electricity. It uses wires to provide a steady flow of electricity.

Electrical current is measured in amperes. Resistors are electrical devices that regulate the flow of electrical current. Resistance is calculated by dividing the voltage of electricity by the current.

1. How can you estimate the resistance?

____

____

2. Use estimation to complete the resistance column of the table.

Resistor	Voltage (volts)	Current (amperes)	Resistance (ohms)
A	2,400	5	
B	3,300	4	
C	4,160	7	
D	6,900	8	

3. **Extension** Explain how you estimated the resistance measurement for Resistor D.

____

____

____

Name ________________________________

Power and Work

Did You Know? A hiker who walks on a trail to the top of a mountain does the same amount of *work* as a mountain climber who climbs to the top of the mountain.

Work describes the amount of energy needed to move an object. Work is measured in joules (J). *Power*, which is measured in watts (W), describes the rate at which the work is done. The formula below shows how power, work, and time are related.

$$\text{power} = \text{work} \div \text{time}$$

The table shows the amounts of work done and the times for different activities.

Activity	Work (J)	Time (s)	Power (W)
Horatio walks up a flight of stairs.	3,125	5	
Becky swims slowly across a pool.	5,310	9	
Ronnie walks across a room.	1,800	6	
Juliana climbs a ladder to the top of a slide.	6,080	8	

1. How can you find the power for each student's activity?

____

2. Use division to complete the power column of the table.

3. **Extension** Estimate by using compatible numbers to check whether your answers in the table are reasonable.

____

____

Name ____________________

Daily Review
5-1

1. Grace was born in 1995. How old will she be in 2027?

Ⓐ 22 years old
Ⓑ 32 years old
Ⓒ 42 years old
Ⓓ 132 years old

2. The art museum provided 147 guided tours in one week. Each guide took 8 people at a time. How many people took the guided tour that week?

Ⓐ 876 people
Ⓑ 1,126 people
Ⓒ 1,176 people
Ⓓ 1,376 people

3. A fabric store receives a shipment of 76 boxes of thread. Each box contains 11 spools of thread. How many spools of thread does the fabric store receive in all?

Ⓐ 836 spools
Ⓑ 736 spools
Ⓒ 502 spools
Ⓓ 87 spools

4. Which comparison is **NOT** true?

Ⓐ 87,254 > 74,316
Ⓑ 12,528 > 12,247
Ⓒ 41,214 < 42,859
Ⓓ 82,493 < 82,395

5. Round 354,738 to the nearest thousand.

____

6. A store has 12 bags of marbles in stock. Each bag has 24 marbles in it. How many marbles are in all of the bags?

____

7. Find 205,048 − 199,355.

____

8. Write 785,420 in expanded for.

____

____

9. In 33,294, how is the value of the 3 in the ten thousands place related to the value of the 3 in the thousands place?

____

____

____

____

____

Name ______________________________

Reteach to Build Understanding
5-1

Vocabulary

1. When you **divide**, you find the number of equal groups or the number of items in each group.

Describe the equation $28 \div 4 = 7$.

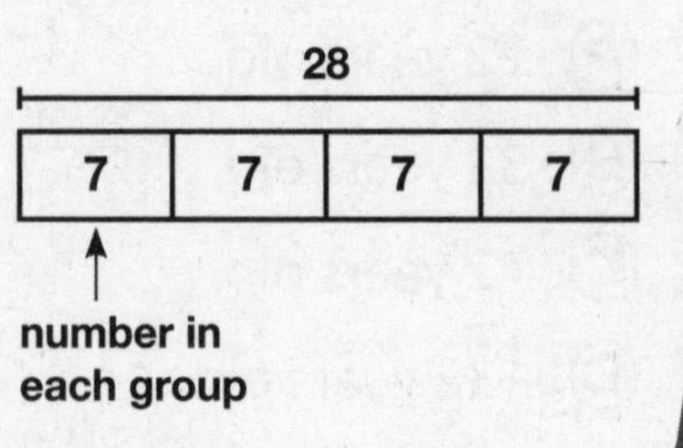

There are ______ items in all.

The items are divided into ______ equal groups.

There are ______ items in each group.

You can use mental math to help divide greater numbers. You can use basic division facts and patterns to help divide mentally.

2. Casper copied 320 pages. He divides the pages equally into 8 packets. How many pages are in each packet?

Find $320 \div 8$.

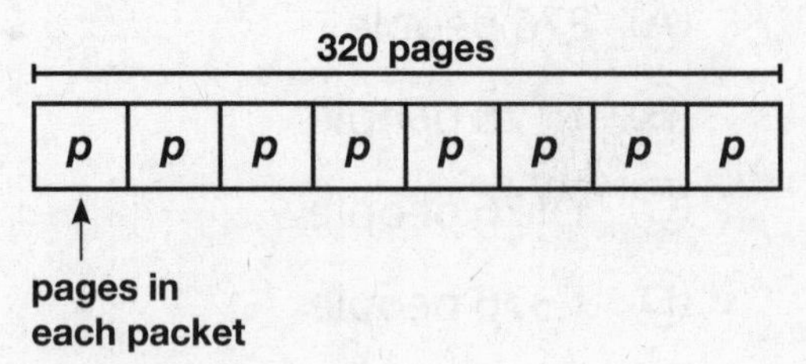

The basic division fact is $32 \div 8 =$ ______.

32 tens $\div 8 =$ ______ tens or ______.

$320 \div 8 =$ ______

There will be ______ pages in each packet.

3. Find $4{,}500 \div 9$.

The basic division fact is ______ $\div 9 =$ ______.

______ hundreds $\div 9 =$ ______ hundreds or ______.

So, $4{,}500 \div 9 =$ ______.

4. Use patterns to find $5{,}600 \div 7$.

$56 \div 7 =$ ______

______ $\div 7 = 80$

$5{,}600 \div 7 =$ ______

5. Use patterns to find $4{,}800 \div 6$.

$48 \div 6 =$ ______

______ $\div 6 = 80$

$4{,}800 \div 6 =$ ______

Use basic facts, patterns, or mental math to find each quotient.

6. $9{,}000 \div 3 =$ ______

7. $640 \div 8 =$ ______

8. $2{,}000 \div 5 =$ ______

On the Back!

9. Use basic facts, patterns, or mental math to find $1{,}200 \div 2$.

Name ______________________________

Read the problem. Then think about each sentence of the problem one at a time. Answer the questions to help solve the problem.

A bakery produced 2 batches of bread with 80 loaves in each batch. It sold 30 loaves each hour. How many loaves of bread were sold in 4 hours? How many loaves of bread were left to sell?

A bakery produced 2 batches of bread with 80 loaves in each batch.

1. How many loaves of bread did the bakery produce in all? Explain.

____

____

It sold 30 loaves each hour.

2. How can you find out how many loaves of bread the bakery sells for any number of hours?

____

How many loaves of bread were sold in 4 hours?

3. Write an expression that can be used to find how many loaves were sold in 4 hours.

____

4. Solve your expression from Exercise 3 to find the number of loaves sold in 4 hours.

____

How many loaves of bread were left to sell?

5. What is the question asking you to find?

____

6. What operation will you use to find the answer?

____

Name ______________________________

Enrichment
5-1

Beth's Best Sellers

The graph below shows Beth's income on the four best-selling books at Beth's Book Store. Divide mentally to answer each question.

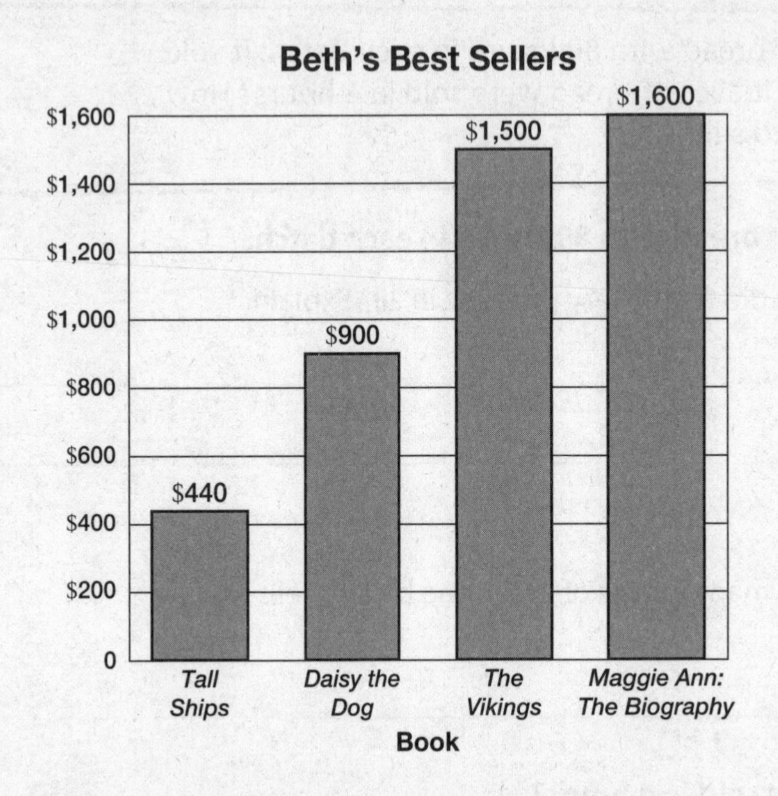

1. Beth charged $8 for each copy of *Maggie Ann: The Biography*. How many total copies did Beth sell? ______________

2. Beth charged $5 for each copy of *The Vikings*. How many total copies did Beth sell? ______________

3. Beth charged $9 for each copy of *Daisy the Dog*. How many total copies did Beth sell? ______________

4. Beth began charging $5 for each copy of *Tall Ships*. She then lowered the price to $4 a copy. How many total copies might Beth have sold? Circle the most reasonable amount listed below.

   70 80 90

5. Which book did Beth sell the most copies of?

____

Name ______________________

Daily Review
5-2

1. Tisha collects old books. She has 2 shelving units, and each shelving unit has 3 shelves. Each shelf holds 12 books. If both shelving units are filled with books, how many books does Tisha have in all?

Ⓐ 72 books
Ⓑ 74 books
Ⓒ 84 books
Ⓓ 144 books

2. Shannon delivered 135 blueberry muffins to each of 7 restaurants. How many muffins did Shannon deliver?

Ⓐ 1,215 muffins
Ⓑ 945 muffins
Ⓒ 915 muffins
Ⓓ 165 muffins

3. Which is **NOT** a way to find 56×9?

Ⓐ $(50 \times 9) + 54$
Ⓑ $(50 + 9) \times (6 + 9)$
Ⓒ $(50 + 6) \times 9$
Ⓓ $(50 \times 9) + (6 \times 9)$

4. The Concord Banquet Hall rents a room for $11,095 for one night. The Falcon Banquet Hall rents a room for $9,876 a night. What is the difference in the prices to rent a room?

Ⓐ $1,219
Ⓑ $1,229
Ⓒ $2,219
Ⓓ $2,221

5. Larry reads the same number of pages each night. After 7 nights, he has read a total of 140 pages. How many pages did Larry read each night?

____

6. The cafeteria ordered 23 boxes of peach yogurt and 57 boxes of raspberry yogurt. Each box contained 6 cups of yogurt. How many cups of yogurt did the cafeteria order?

____

7. Ms. Burke buys 13 packets of 27 flower seeds and 26 packets of 12 vegetable seeds for her science class. How many seeds does Ms. Burke purchase? Show your work.

____

____

____

____

____

8. Kendra's family plans a trip that is 600 miles long. If they drive the same number of miles each day for 6 days, how many miles will they drive each day?

____

Name ______________________________

Reteach to Build Understanding
5-2

Vocabulary

1. **Compatible numbers** are numbers that are easy to compute mentally. Compatible numbers can be used to estimate quotients.

   Use compatible numbers to estimate 58 ÷ 8.

   Think of a multiplication fact with 8 as a factor that has a product that is close to 58.

   8 × 6 = ______ 8 × 7 = ______ 8 × 8 = ______

   ______ is close to 58, so divide ______ by 8.

   ______ ÷ 8 = ______

   So, 58 ÷ 8 is about = ______.

2. Use compatible numbers to estimate 267 ÷ 3.

   What number is close to 267 and is easy to divide by 3?
   Use multiples of 10 that are close to 267.

   Is 260 easily divided by 3? Think 26 ÷ 3.
   Since the quotient has a remainder, 26 and 3 are not compatible.

   Is 270 easily divided by 3? Think 27 ÷ 3. ______

   ______ ÷ 3 = ______

   So, 267 ÷ 3 is about ______.

Use compatible numbers to estimate each quotient.

3. 375 ÷ 6 ________________

4. 606 ÷ 3 ________________

5. 48 ÷ 5 ________________

6. 277 ÷ 7 ________________

7. 595 ÷ 6 ________________

On the Back!

8. Use compatible numbers to estimate 148 ÷ 5. Show your work.

Name ________________________________

Build Mathematical Literacy
5-2

Read the problem. Answer the questions to help understand how to solve the problem.

The International Space Station takes 644 minutes to orbit Earth 7 times. About how long does each orbit take?

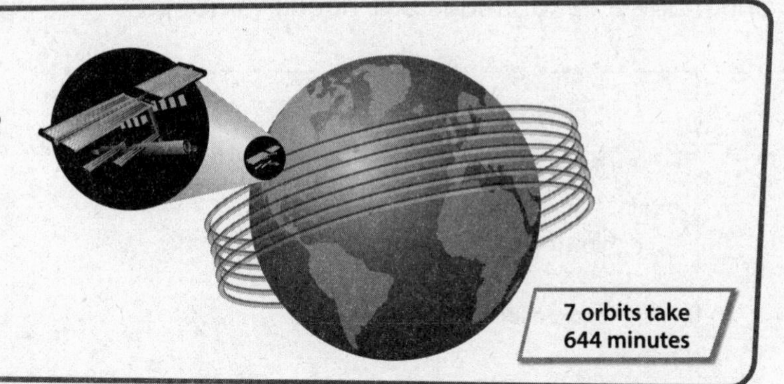

What do you **KNOW** from the information stated in the problem?	
WHERE can you find the information you need to solve the problem?	
WHAT exactly does the problem want you to find?	
What **STRATEGY** or operation will you use to solve this problem?	
How does the use of the word *about* in the question affect the strategy you choose to solve the problem?	

Name

Tanya's To-Do List

Tanya wants to get a lot done this weekend.
She made a list of things she needs to do.

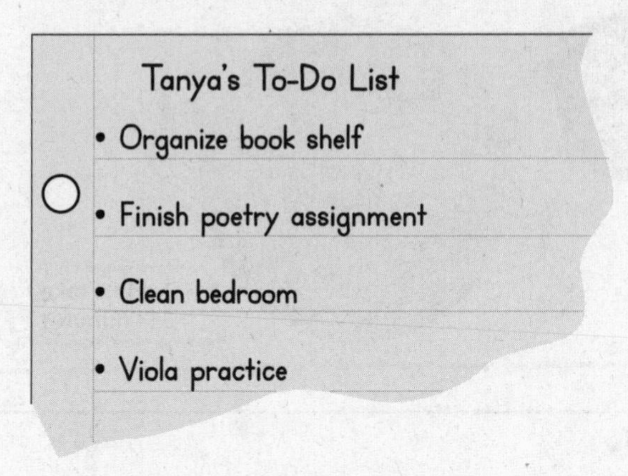

Tanya's To-Do List
• Organize book shelf
• Finish poetry assignment
• Clean bedroom
• Viola practice

1. Tanya wants to place 209 books on her bookcase. The bookcase has 4 shelves. About how many books will she place on each shelf?

2. Tanya has to write a poem with 175 words. She plans to spend 2 hours writing. About how many words should she write each hour to finish the poem?

3. Tanya wants to spend an equal amount of time cleaning her closet, her drawers, and under her bed. If she has put aside 95 minutes to do this, about how much time can she spend on each area?

4. Tanya's goal is to practice her viola for 139 minutes over 2 days. About how many minutes will she practice each day?

Name ______________________

Daily Review

5-3

1. The Smith family is packing to move. There are 238 books to pack into moving boxes. Each box holds 8 books. About how many moving boxes will be needed to pack the books?

Ⓐ About 30 boxes

Ⓑ About 20 boxes

Ⓒ About 10 boxes

Ⓓ About 8 boxes

2. A salesman drives 2,100 miles each month. How many miles does the salesman drive in 4 months?

Ⓐ 840 miles

Ⓑ 850 miles

Ⓒ 8,400 miles

Ⓓ 8,500 miles

3. Antonio runs 4 miles each day. How many miles does he run in one year? Remember, one year has 365 days.

Ⓐ 2,240 miles

Ⓑ 1,640 miles

Ⓒ 1,460 miles

Ⓓ 1,240 miles

4. There are 357 people signed up to attend a fund-raiser dinner. The hall can seat 6 people at each table. About how many tables will be needed?

Ⓐ About 50 tables

Ⓑ About 60 tables

Ⓒ About 70 tables

Ⓓ About 80 tables

5. Joe does 140 push-ups and 150 sit-ups each day. How many push-ups and sit-ups will Joe do in 5 days?

____

6. Estimate the quotient.
$555 \div 8$

____

7. Marissa is planning a community picnic. She has 35 tomatoes that can each be cut into 7 slices. How many tomato slices will Marissa have?

____

8. Draw an area model to show how to use the Distributive Property to find 26×39.

9. Find $200{,}000 - 168{,}219$.

____

Name ___________________________

Reteach to Build Understanding
5-3

Vocabulary

1. **Rounding** is a process that determines which multiple of 10, 100, 1,000, and so on a number is closest to.

   Round each number to the nearest thousand.

   5,982 rounds to __________.

   4,239 rounds to __________.

   Round each number to the nearest hundred.

   3,529 rounds to __________.

   6,284 rounds to __________.

You can use rounding or compatible numbers to estimate quotients.

2. Estimate 3,742 ÷ 8 by rounding the dividend.

   Round 3,742 to the nearest thousand. __________

   Use the rounded dividend to estimate the quotient.

   __________ ÷ 8 = __________

   So, 3,742 ÷ 8 is about __________.

3. Estimate 2,389 ÷ 3 by rounding the dividend.

   Round 2,389 to the nearest hundred. __________

   Use the rounded dividend to estimate the quotient.

   __________ ÷ 3 = __________

   So, 2,389 ÷ 3 is about __________.

Estimate each quotient.

4. 2,782 ÷ 7 ______________
5. 3,578 ÷ 6 ______________
6. 3,099 ÷ 3 ______________

On the Back!

7. Use rounding to estimate 1,769 ÷ 3. Explain.

Name ____________________

Read the problem. Answer the questions to help you solve the problem.

Laura's dog eats 1 bag of dog food every 6 days. About how many bags will her dog eat in 1 year? About how many bags will Laura's dog eat in 10 years? Explain.

Before reading: Preview, predict, and set purpose.

1. What is the problem about?

2. How many questions will you need to answer to solve the problem? What are they?

During reading: Check understanding; identify key information.

3. Underline the information from the problem that you will need to use to solve the problem.

4. How does the use of the word *about* in the problem affect the process you use when solving the problem?

After reading: Summarize and evaluate.

5. How did you find how many bags of food Laura's dog eats in a year?

Name ______________________

Enrichment **5-3**

Estimating Bracelets

Carla and Marla are making bracelets to sell at a craft fair. Each bracelet uses 5 blue beads, 8 silver beads, 2 gold beads, and 6 opal beads. The table shows how many beads they have of each color.

- Use estimation to figure out about how many bracelets Carla and Marla can make with each color of bead.
- Then tell if each answer is an **overestimate** and they will not have quite enough beads, or an **underestimate** and they will have some beads left over.

Color	Number of Beads	Number Needed for Each Bracelet	About How Many Bracelets They Can Make	Is the Estimate Over or Under?
Blue	225	5		
Silver	422	8		
Gold	55	2		
Opal	225	6		

1. About how many bracelets can they make before they run out of beads?

____

2. What color will they run out of first?

____

3. Will they run out of blue beads or opal beads first? How do you know?

____

____

Name ______________________

1. Isabelle scored 528 points and Brandy scored 285 points in the same game. Which is the best estimate for the total number of points scored by the two girls?

Ⓐ About 800 points

Ⓑ About 700 points

Ⓒ About 500 points

Ⓓ About 300 points

2. Which expression does the array show?

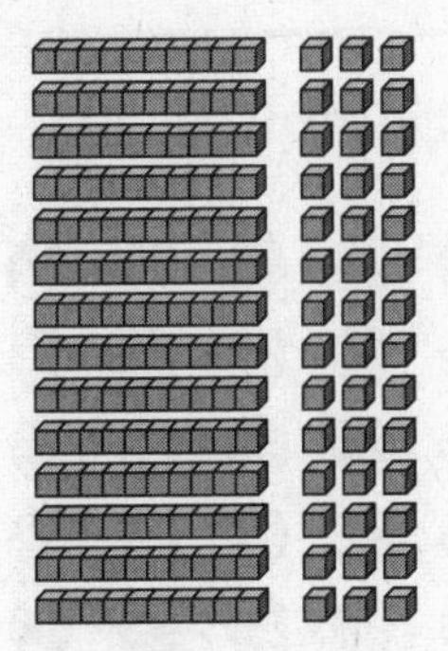

Ⓐ 10×3

Ⓑ 14×10

Ⓒ 14×13

Ⓓ $(14 \times 10) + (3 \times 10)$

3. What is the perimeter of the figure shown below?

12 in.

10 in.

Ⓐ 22 inches

Ⓑ 44 inches

Ⓒ 120 inches

Ⓓ 240 inches

4. A new car costs $23,649. The car dealership has an end-of-the-year sale, and the car will be priced at $22,399. How much money can a customer save by purchasing the car on sale?

____

5. Explain how you could use compatible numbers to estimate $245 \div 3$. Then estimate the quotient.

____

____

____

____

____

6. Explain how to use basic facts and number patterns to find $5{,}600 \div 7$.

____

____

____

____

7. Round 389,735 to the nearest thousand.

____

Name ______________________

Vocabulary

1. The **remainder** is the number that remains after the division is complete. Use an R to indicate the remainder.

Tia has 26 walnuts. She gives 7 walnuts to each friend. How many friends get 7 walnuts? How many walnuts are left over?

Use the array to find $26 \div 7$. Circle the groups of 7.

There are ______ groups of 7.

There are ______ left over.

$26 \div 7 =$ ______

______ friends each get 7 walnuts.

There are ______ walnuts left over.

2. Juan puts 57 oranges in bags. Each bag holds 6 oranges. Use the array to divide.

To find $57 \div 6$, circle groups of ______.

$57 \div 6 =$ ______

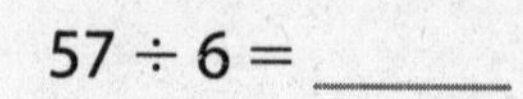

How many full bags of oranges are there?

____

How many oranges are not in bags?

____

How many bags does Juan need to put all the oranges in bags? ______ bags

3. How many craft sticks will be left over if 9 friends equally share a package of 85 craft sticks? ______________

4. A group of 43 people are going to a concert. If 6 people fit in each car, how many cars will they need to take? ____________

5. Bess has 19 sunflowers that she is putting into vases. She will put 4 sunflowers in each vase. How many vases will have 4 flowers? ____________

On the Back!

6. Find the number of equal groups and the number left over for $88 \div 3$. Show your work.

Name ______________________________

Read the problem. Answer the questions to help you understand the problem.

Higher Order Thinking Write a problem that requires adding 1 to the quotient when interpreting the remainder.

1. In $36 \div 4 = 9$, identify the *dividend*, *divisor*, and *quotient*.

____

____

2. Suppose you need to determine how many teams you can make if there are 5 people on each team. Explain why there could be a remainder.

____

____

3. Given the context from Exercise 2, would it make sense to add 1 to the quotient when interpreting the remainder? Explain.

____

____

____

4. Describe a new division context in which it ***would*** make sense to add 1 to the quotient when interpreting the remainder.

____

____

Name ______________________________

Will They Reach the Top?

Begin at the bottom of each mountain and solve each division problem. If there is a remainder, the hiker stops at that problem. If there is no remainder, the hiker keeps climbing.

1.

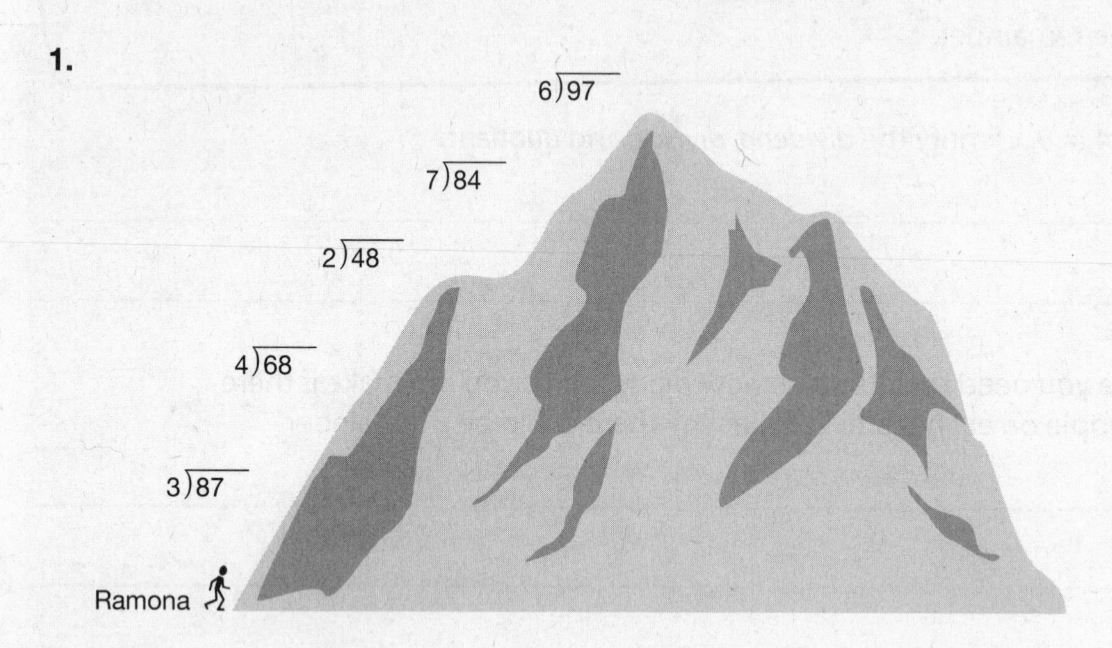

2.

5)95

5)74

6)78

4)72

3)51

Gordon

3. Which hiker made it farther up the mountain?

____

Name ___

Daily Review
5-5

1. Wayne bought 6 tickets for a championship football game. Each ticket cost $159. How much money did Wayne spend?

Ⓐ $604
Ⓑ $904
Ⓒ $948
Ⓓ $954

2. There are 35 boxes of soup cans on a delivery truck. How many cans of soup are on the delivery truck if there are 30 cans in each box?

Ⓐ 1,050 cans
Ⓑ 850 cans
Ⓒ 625 cans
Ⓓ 425 cans

3. Andrea reads 36 pages each night. How many pages does Andrea read in 42 nights?

Ⓐ 1,502 pages
Ⓑ 1,512 pages
Ⓒ 1,552 pages
Ⓓ 1,582 pages

4. Select all the expressions that have an estimated quotient near 500.

☐ $4,000 \div 6$
☐ $4,103 \div 8$
☐ $3,420 \div 7$
☐ $1,489 \div 3$
☐ $455 \div 9$

5. Daniel recycles 48 aluminum cans each week. How many cans does Daniel recycle in 51 weeks?

___

6. Mugs cost $6 each. Marc has $485 to spend on mugs for his company. About how many mugs can Marc buy for his company?

___

7. Richard ran 8 laps around a 400-meter track. How many meters did Richard run in all?

___

8. Round 6,852 to the nearest thousand.

___

9. Write the number name and expanded form for 503,672.

___

___

___

___

Name ______________________

Reteach to Build Understanding
5-5

Vocabulary

1. **Partial quotients** show the separate parts of the answer to a division problem. The sum of the partial quotients is the quotient.

$$\begin{array}{r} 7 \\ 10 \\ 5\overline{)85} \\ -50 \\ \hline 35 \\ -35 \\ \hline 0 \end{array}$$
(7 and 10: partial quotients)

The partial quotients are ______ and ______.

The quotient is ______.

2. Use partial quotients to find 70 ÷ 5.

Estimate: How many 5s are in 70?

10 groups of ______ is ______. Subtract.

How many 5s are in 20?

4 groups of ______ is ______. Subtract.

$$\begin{array}{r} \square \\ \square \\ 5\overline{)70} \\ -50 \\ \hline 20 \\ -20 \\ \hline 0 \end{array}$$

The partial quotients are ______ and ______.
Add the partial quotients to find the quotient.

So, 70 ÷ 5 = ______.

3. Use partial quotients to find 80 ÷ 5.
Show your work.

80 ÷ 5 = ______

$$\begin{array}{r} \square \\ \square \\ 5\overline{)80} \\ -\square \\ \hline \square \\ -\square \\ \hline \square \end{array}$$

4. Use partial quotients to find 92 ÷ 4.
Show your work.

92 ÷ 4 = ______

On the Back!

5. Use partial quotients to find 96 ÷ 6. Show your work.

Name ________________________________

Build Mathematical Literacy
5-5

Read the problem. Answer the questions to help understand the problem.

Higher Order Thinking Amanda wants to put some of her books on 4 shelves with 6 books on each shelf, and the rest on 6 shelves with 3 books on each shelf. Can Amanda arrange her books this way? Explain.

42 books

Before reading: Preview, predict, and set purpose.

1. What is the problem about?

____

2. What specific question will the solution answer?

____

____

During reading: Check understanding; identify key information.

3. Highlight the information from the text of the problem that you will need to use to solve the problem.

4. Is all of the information that you need to solve the problem in the text of the problem? Explain.

____

____

After reading: Summarize and evaluate.

5. Reread the question. Should your answer be numerical? Explain.

____

____

Name ___________________________

Enrichment
5-5

Division Amazement

1. Trace a path to the middle of the maze. You can pass through a wall only where the remainder is 2 when you divide.

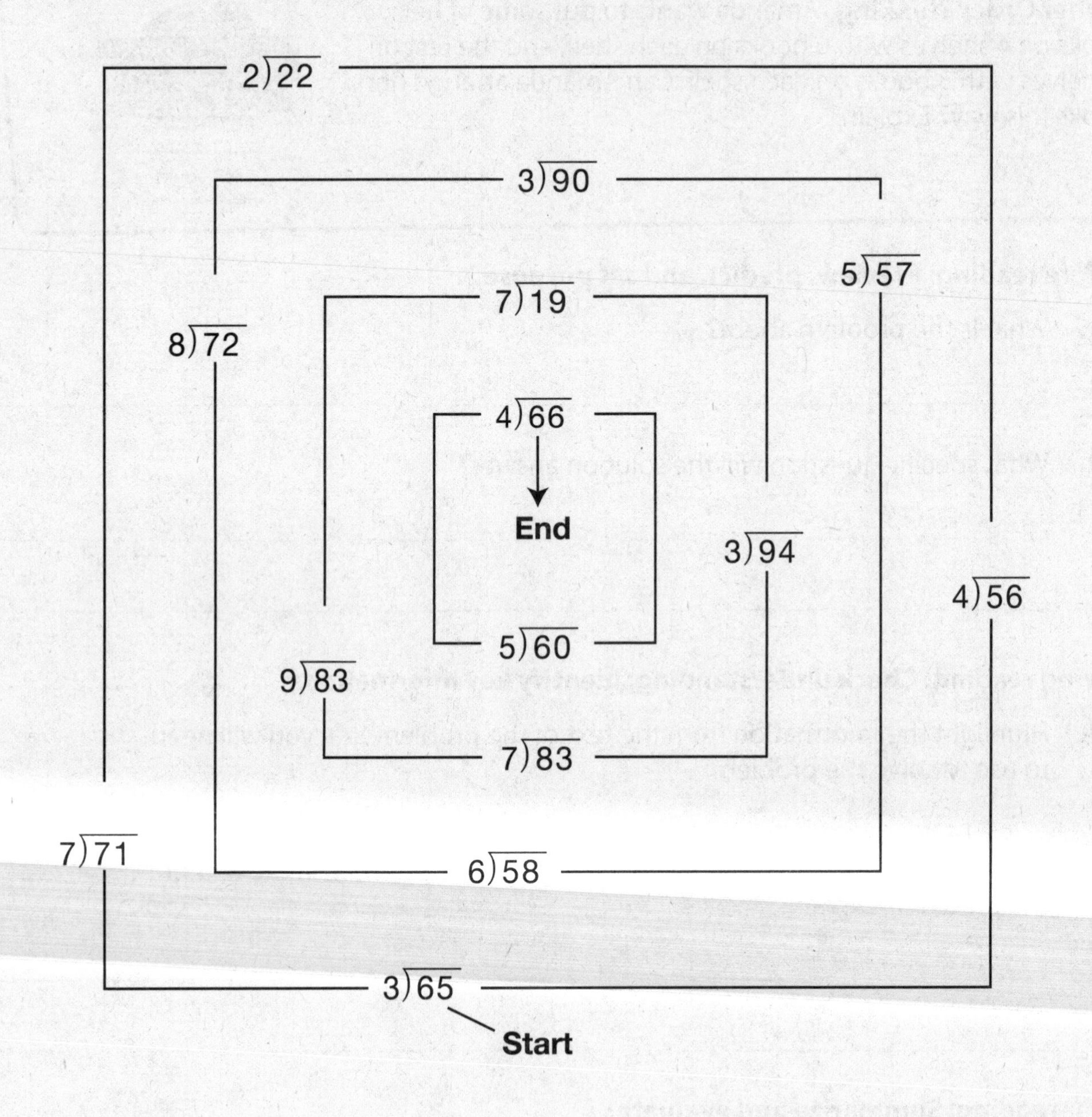

2. Solve **only** the problem described. **a.** 2)91 **b.** 4)58 **c.** 8)79

- The quotient has 2 digits.
- The remainder is greater than 1.

Name ______________________________

Daily Review
5-6

1. Alexandra has 24 vases. There are 17 flowers in each vase. How many flowers are in all of the vases?

Ⓐ 41 flowers
Ⓑ 192 flowers
Ⓒ 408 flowers
Ⓓ 428 flowers

2. Diana wants to save a total of $1,500 to buy a laptop computer. If she saves $5 per week, in how many weeks will Diana be able to buy the computer?

Ⓐ 3 weeks
Ⓑ 30 weeks
Ⓒ 300 weeks
Ⓓ 3,000 weeks

3. Manny has 67 coins in his collection. He can display 6 coins on one tray. How many trays will Manny need to display all of his coins?

Ⓐ 12 trays
Ⓑ 11 trays
Ⓒ 7 trays
Ⓓ 6 trays

4. Select all the numbers which are the partial products for $6 \times 2,189$?

☐ 54
☐ 480
☐ 600
☐ 1,200
☐ 12,000

5. Sophia is scheduled to work 4 hours each day, Monday through Friday. She also works 8 hours on Saturday. She has 4 weeks off work each year. How many hours will Sophia work in one year? Remember, there are 52 weeks in one year.

____

6. Henry wants to buy a set of speakers that cost $325. So far, he has saved $157. How much more does Henry have to save to buy the speakers?

____

7. Heather used a basic fact to complete the equation below. What is the missing number? Explain how you can use a basic fact to find the missing number.

$4,200 \div \square = 700$

____

____

____

____

____

____

____

Name ______________________

Reteach to Build Understanding
5-6

Vocabulary

1. You can use **estimation,** or find an approximate value for 165 ÷ 4.

   Estimate the quotient. How many 4s are in 165?
   Multiply:

   4 × 30 = ________ 4 × 40 = ________ 4 × 50 = ________

   Which product is closest to, but not greater than, the dividend? ________

   165 ÷ 4 is ____________.

Use estimation and partial quotients to find 2,458 ÷ 5.

2. How many 5s are in 2,458?
   Multiply:

   300 × 5 = ________

   400 × 5 = ________

   500 × 5 = ________

   500 is too many. Use ________.

   How many 5s are in 458?
   Multiply:

   80 × 5 = ________

   90 × 5 = ________

   100 × 5 = ________

   ________ is too many. Use ________.

   How many 5s are in 8?
   Multiply:

   1 × 5 = ______

   2 × 5 = ______

   ______ is too many. Use ______.

   The remainder, ______ is less than the divisor, ______, so there are no more 5s in 2,458.

   2,458 ÷ 5 = __________

```
           □
         □ □  } partial quotients
       □ 0 0
  5)2, 4 5 8
  - 2, 0 0 0
       □ □ □
     - □ □ □
           8
         - □
           □
```

On the Back!

3. Use partial quotients to divide 498 ÷ 6. Show your work.

Name ___________________________

Read the problem. For each question choose where you can find the information.

Higher Order Thinking How many headbands can the students make? Explain.

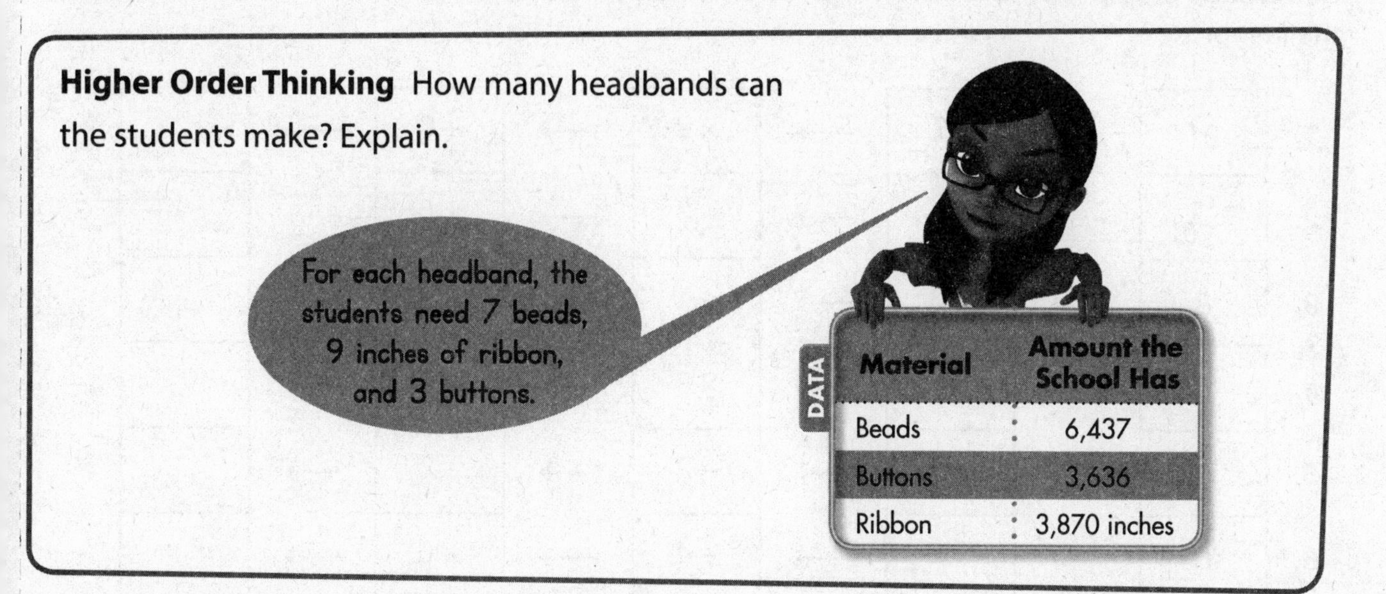
For each headband, the students need 7 beads, 9 inches of ribbon, and 3 buttons.
DATA

Material	Amount the School Has
Beads	6,437
Buttons	3,636
Ribbon	3,870 inches

1. Where is the question in this problem?

Ⓐ In the problem text
Ⓑ In the speech bubble
Ⓒ In the data table
Ⓓ It is not explicitly stated in the text, the speech bubble, or the data table.

2. Where can you find the number of beads and buttons and the length of ribbon needed to make each headband?

Ⓐ In the problem text
Ⓑ In the speech bubble
Ⓒ In the data table
Ⓓ It is not explicitly stated in the text, the speech bubble, or the data table.

3. Where can you find the amount of each material that the school already has?

Ⓐ In the problem text
Ⓑ In the speech bubble
Ⓒ In the data table
Ⓓ It is not explicitly stated in the text, the speech bubble, or the data table.

4. Where can you find the operation or operations that you will need to solve the problem?

Ⓐ In the problem text
Ⓑ In the speech bubble
Ⓒ In the data table
Ⓓ It is not explicitly stated in the text, the speech bubble, or the data table.

Name ______________________________

Enrichment
5-6

Fact Path

Solve each problem by following the arrows. Write the final answer in the last box.

1.	21	→	÷ 7	→	× 2	→	÷ 6	→	
2.	54	→	÷ 6	→	÷ 3	→	× 5	→	
3.	8	→	× 3	→	÷ 4	→	× 7	→	
4.	5	→	÷ 5	→	× 9	→	× 4	→	
5.	72	→	÷ 9	→	÷ 2	→	÷ 2	→	
6.	6	→	× 2	→	÷ 4	→	× 6	→	
7.	30	→	÷ 5	→	× 0	→	× 8	→	
8.	8	→	× 3	→	÷ 6	→	+ 5	→	
9.	35	→	÷ 7	→	+ 4	→	× 9	→	
10.	4	→	× 7	→	− 3	→	÷ 5	→	

Write two fact paths. Include a multiplication step and a division step in each path.

11.		→		→		→		→	
12.		→		→		→		→	

Name ______________________

1. Taylor rides her bicycle 108 miles each week. How many miles does Taylor ride in 4 weeks?

Ⓐ 408 miles
Ⓑ 412 miles
Ⓒ 422 miles
Ⓓ 432 miles

2. Which place should you use to compare the following numbers?

394,162 and 389,440

Ⓐ Hundreds
Ⓑ Thousands
Ⓒ Ten thousands
Ⓓ Hundred thousands

3. Tia learned to spell 1,200 words in 4 weeks for a spelling bee. She learned the same number of words each week. How many words did Tia learn each week?

Ⓐ 300 words
Ⓑ 600 words
Ⓒ 3,000 words
Ⓓ 4,800 words

4. Which partial products are needed to find the final product? Select all that apply.

☐ 8
☐ 16
☐ 18
☐ 80
☐ 100

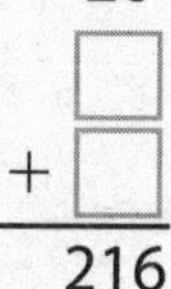

5. Use compatible numbers to estimate 132 ÷ 7. Explain your reasoning.

____
____
____

6. Stacy works 22 hours per week. Daniel works 26 hours per week. How many more hours does Daniel work than Stacy in 6 weeks? Show how you solved the problem.

____
____
____
____
____
____

7. The total cost of a washing machine and a clothes dryer is $2,480. The cost of the clothes dryer is $899. Write and solve an equation to find *c*, the cost of the washing machine.

____
____
____

Name ______________________________

Reteach to Build Understanding
5-7

Vocabulary

1. **Equal groups** are groups that have the same number of items. When you divide, you find the number in each equal group or the number of equal groups.

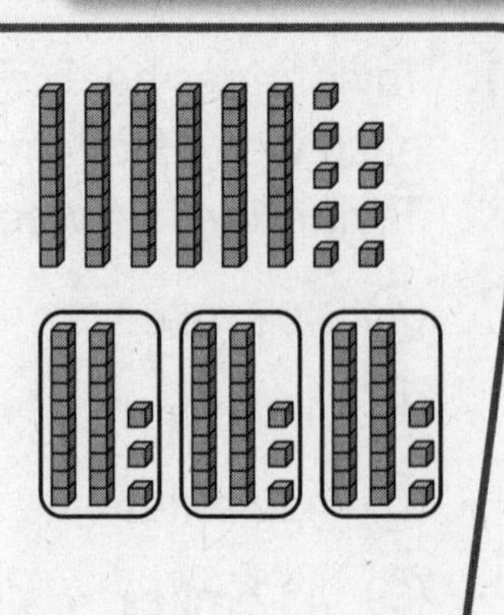

What number is shown by the place-value blocks? _____

What number does each equal group show? _____

How many equal groups are there? _____

Write a division sentence for the model. _____ ÷ 3 = _____

Use the place-value drawing at the right to find 443 ÷ 3. Draw pictures to solve.

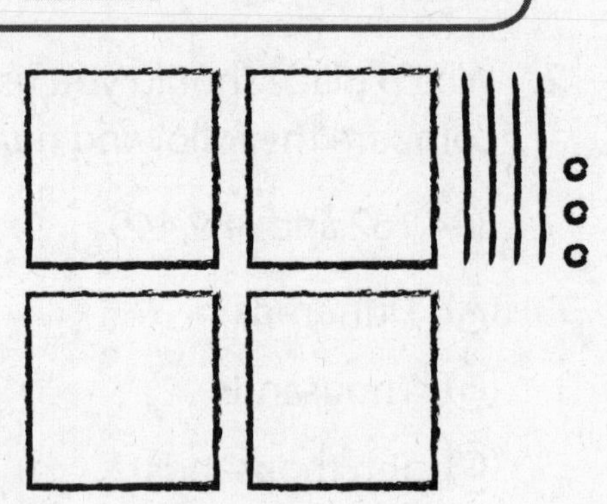

2. Divide the hundreds into three equal groups.

There is _____ hundred in each of the 3 groups.

There is _____ hundred remaining.
Unbundle the remaining hundred.

_____ hundred = _____ tens

10 tens + 4 tens = _____ tens

3. Divide the tens into three equal groups.

There are _____ tens in each of the 3 groups.

There are _____ tens remaining.
Unbundle the remaining tens.

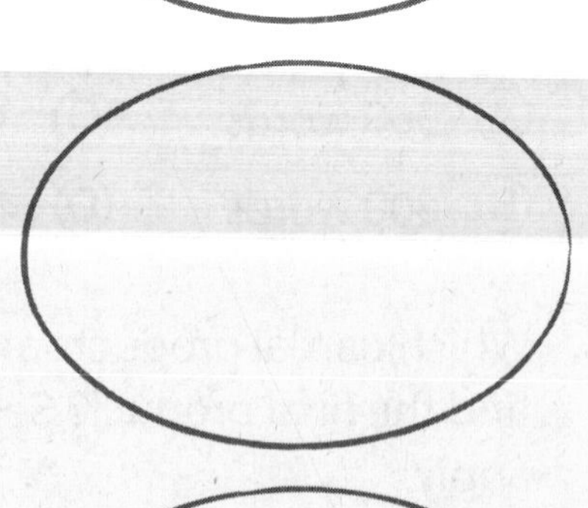

_____ tens = _____ ones

20 ones + _____ ones = _____ ones

4. Divide the ones into three equal groups.

There are _____ ones in each of the 3 groups.

There are _____ ones remaining.

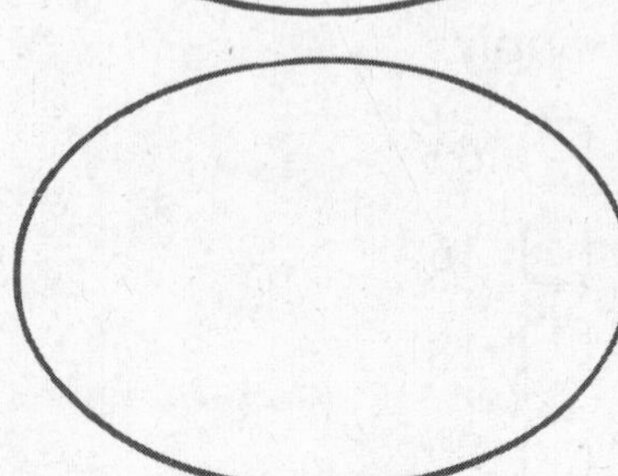

5. 443 ÷ 3 = __________

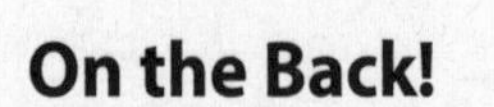

On the Back!

6. Find 59 ÷ 4. Draw pictures to solve. Show your work.

Name ____________________

Read the problem. Answer the questions to help you think about how to use a drawing to represent the problem.

Maya used a drawing to divide 86. She made groups of 17 with 1 left over. Draw a picture to determine how many groups Maya made.

1. What part of a division problem does the number 86 represent?

2. How will the number 86 be represented in your drawing?

3. What part of a division problem does the 17 represent?

4. How will the number 17 be represented in your drawing?

5. What part of a division problem does the number 1 represent?

6. How will the number 1 be represented in your drawing?

7. Which part of the division problem is not part of the given information in the text? How will it be represented in your drawing?

Name ______________________

Division Star

Divide. Write the quotient in the large circle. Write the remainder, if there is one, in the small circle.

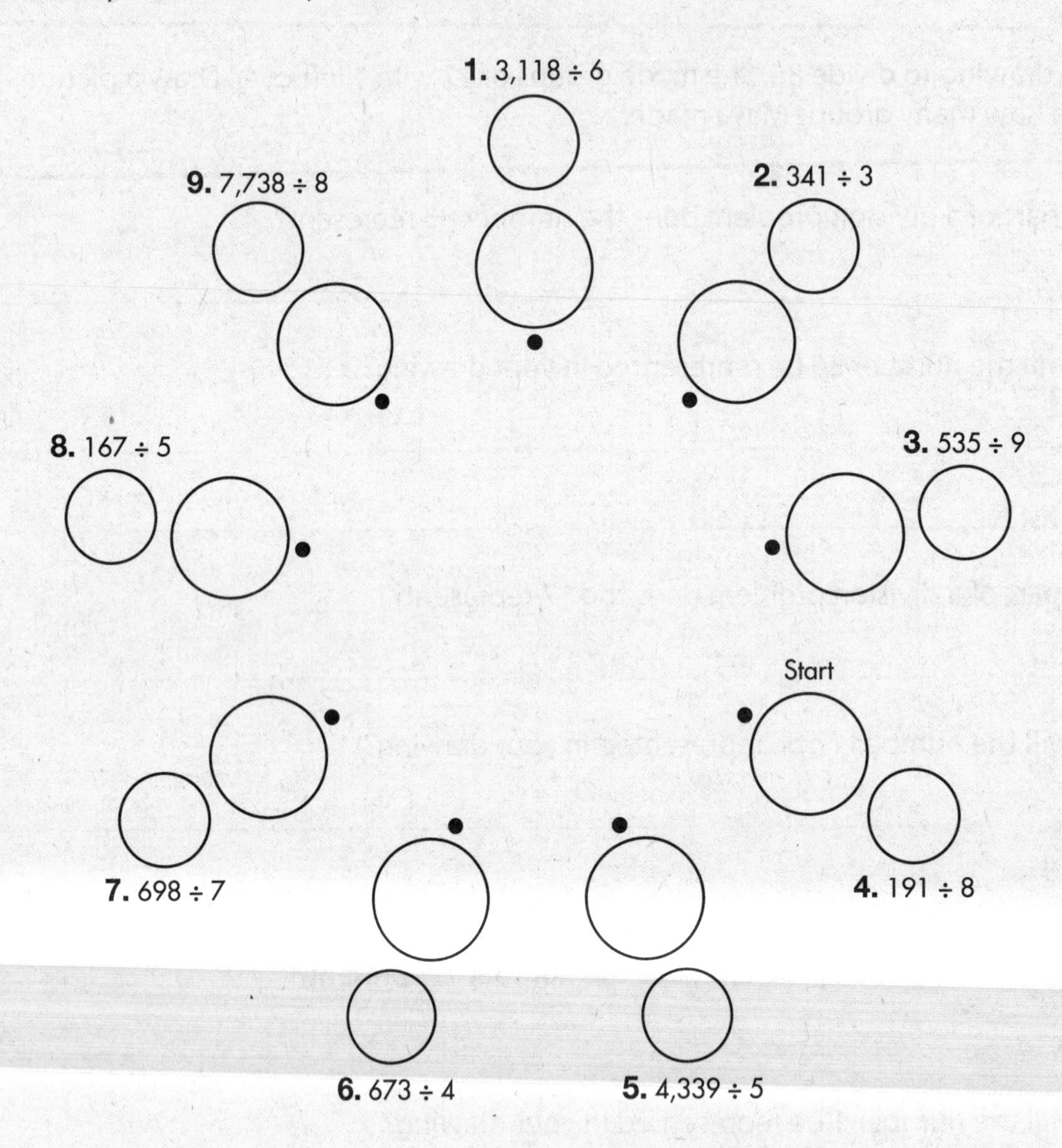

Start with the least quotient. Use a ruler to draw a line from each quotient to the next greater one. Connect the greatest quotient to the one with which you started.

10. What is the shape you drew? ______________________

Name ____________________

Daily Review

5-8

1. Nola earns $62 per week walking dogs. How much money does Nola make in one year? Remember, one year has 52 weeks.

Ⓐ $3,442

Ⓑ $3,224

Ⓒ $3,124

Ⓓ $2,134

2. An exercise class costs $9 per class. Seven students are planning to take 12 classes. How much will the students pay in all?

Ⓐ $189

Ⓑ $715

Ⓒ $756

Ⓓ $1,260

3. Benny has 79 model cars. He wants to give them to 4 of his friends. He wants each friend to have an equal number of cars. How many model cars will Benny have left over?

Ⓐ 0 model cars

Ⓑ 1 model car

Ⓒ 2 model cars

Ⓓ 3 model cars

4. In which number is the value of the digit in the thousands place ten times as great as the value of the digit in the hundreds place?

Ⓐ 22,876

Ⓑ 34,452

Ⓒ 60,671

Ⓓ 79,740

5. Sayid wants to buy 3 sweaters for $37 each and 2 scarves for $11 each. How much will Sayid spend on these pieces of clothing?

____

6. Mandi has $52 and would like to buy some magazines. Each magazine costs $8. How many magazines can Mandi buy? How much more money would she need to buy another magazine?

____

____

____

____

7. Round 9,870 to the nearest hundred.

____

8. Sarah has collected 34 sports cards. She shares them equally with her sister. How many sports cards does Sarah give her sister?

____

9. Write 76,732 in expanded form.

____

____

Name ______________________________

Reteach to Build Understanding
5-8

Vocabulary

1. An estimate is used to check the **reasonableness** of an answer. First estimate, then divide. The quotient is reasonable if it is close to the estimate.

Estimate 126 ÷ 6.

126 is close to ______.

Divide ______ ÷ ______ = ______

126 ÷ 6 = 21

Is 21 close to 20? ______

Estimate 246 ÷ 6.

246 is close to ______.

Divide ______ ÷ ______ = ______

246 ÷ 6 = 41

Is 41 close to 40? ______

Divide. Check for reasonableness.

2. 65 ÷ 3

Estimate: ______________________________

Divide the tens.

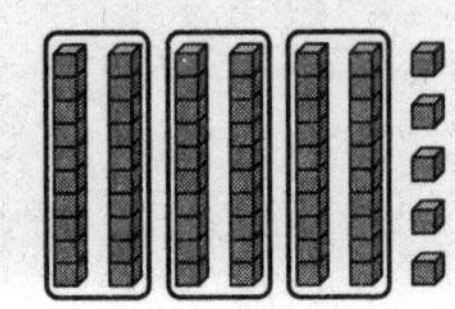

6 tens divided into 3 equal groups.

______ tens are in each group.

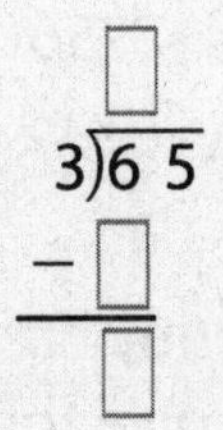

3. Divide the ones.

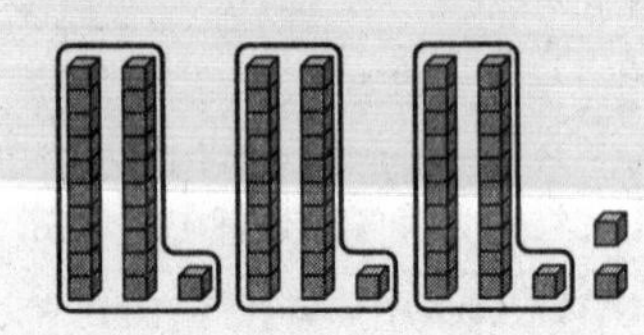

Divide the ones. ______ ones divided into 3 equal groups. There are 2 ones left over.

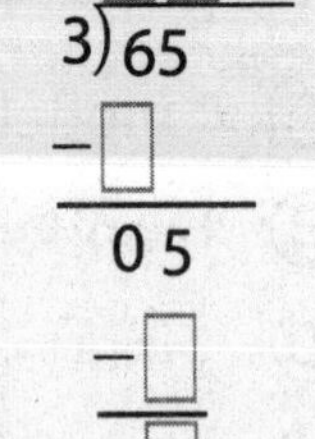

4. Is the estimate close to the quotient?

____

On the Back!

5. Find 526 ÷ 6. Show your work.

Name ______________________

Build Mathematical Literacy
5-8

Read the problem. Answer the questions to help you solve the problem.

Higher Order Thinking Maggie is making trail mix. She makes 4 batches of the recipe shown. She divides the batches into 3 equal-sized bags. How many ounces are in each bag?

DATA

Tasty Trail Mix	
Granola	8 oz
Nuts	5 oz
Raisins	2 oz
Cranberries	3 oz

1. What does the problem ask you to find?

____

2. What other question or questions will need to be answered before you can answer the question the problem asks?

____

____

3. What does the table show?

____

____

4. Can you answer the question(s) in Exercise 2 using only the information in the table? Explain.

____

____

5. Underline the numerical information from the text that you will need to use to solve the problem.

6. What operations will you use to solve the problem?

____

Name ______________________________

Follow the Money Trail

Each trail below has money that you collect as you walk. At the end of each trail, the total amount of money is divided by a divisor. You receive the quotient.

1. \$100 + \$100 + \$500 + \$500 = ______ ÷ 2 = ______

2.

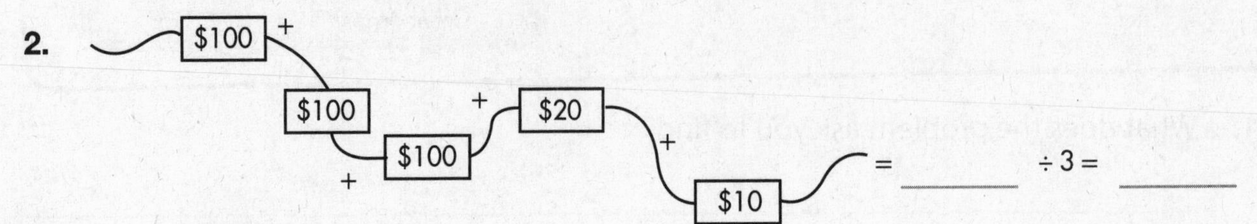

3.

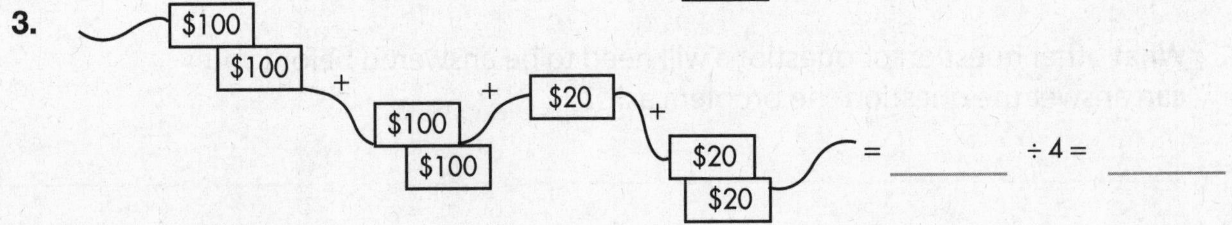

4.

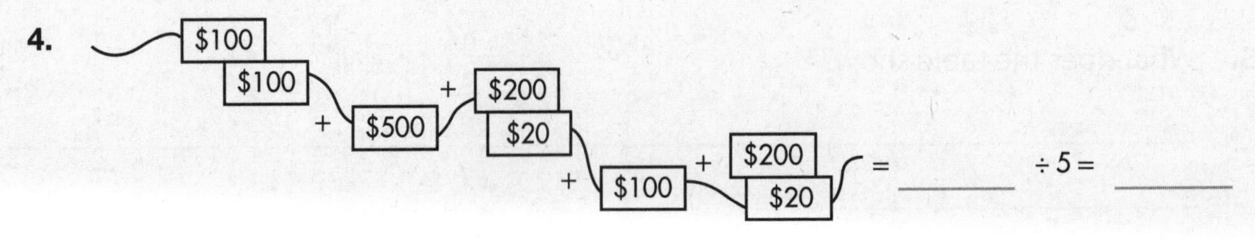

5.

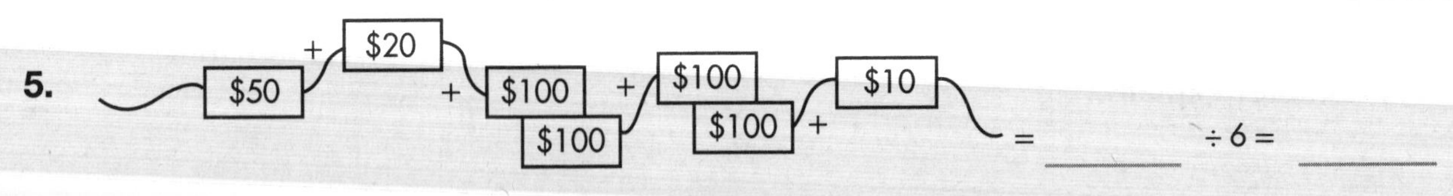

6. \$100 \$100 + \$50 \$50 + \$100 + \$20 \$20 + \$50 = ______ ÷ 7 = ______

Name ______________________

Daily Review
5-9

1. Which shows nine hundred seventy-five thousand, eight hundred forty-one using base-ten numerals?

Ⓐ 995,841
Ⓑ 975,841
Ⓒ 975,840
Ⓓ 900,840

2. A news article reported that 22,004 adults and 12,036 children attended a local fair. How many adults and children attended in all?

Ⓐ 34,030
Ⓑ 34,040
Ⓒ 34,304
Ⓓ 34,400

3. There were 165 students going on a field trip. Each van can carry 8 students. How many vans will be needed for the field trip?

Ⓐ 21 vans
Ⓑ 20 vans
Ⓒ 12 vans
Ⓓ 8 vans

4. Which is **NOT** a way to multiply mentally to find 4×225?

Ⓐ $(4 \times 200) + (4 \times 25)$
Ⓑ $(4 \times 200) + (4 \times 20) + (4 \times 5)$
Ⓒ $(2 + 2) \times (200 + 25)$
Ⓓ $(4 \times 200) + 100$

5. A museum sells sets of 4 crystals as shown below. They sell 224 crystals one weekend. How many sets of crystals do they sell?

____

6. Arthur, Jorge, and Dylan collected a total of 328 cans to recycle. Arthur collected 105 and Jorge collected 112. How many cans did Dylan collect?

____

7. Find the quotient.

$2{,}482 \div 7 =$ ☐ R ☐

8. Compare.

$3{,}012 + 1{,}799$ ◯ $99 + 4{,}712$

9. What are partial products for 35×56?

____

10. What is the missing factor?

$3 \times$ ______ $= 738$

11. What is the value of the 4 in 645,079?

____

Name ______________________

Reteach to Build Understanding
5-9

Vocabulary

1. **Compatible numbers** are numbers that are easy to compute mentally. To estimate a quotient, you can use compatible numbers.

   Use compatible numbers to estimate 3,102 ÷ 8.

   3,200 and 8 are compatible numbers because they can be easily divided.

   Estimate: ________ ÷ ________ = ________

   So, 3,102 ÷ 8 is about ________.

2. Estimate 7,809 ÷ 8.

   8,000 ÷ 8 = ________

3. Use partial quotients to find 7,809 ÷ 8.
   Show your work at the right.
   78 hundreds ÷ 8 is about 9 hundreds.

4. Estimate how many 8s are in ________.

   8 × ______ = ________

5. Estimate how many 8s are in ________.
   8 × 6 = 48

   Write any leftovers as the remainder.

   7,809 ÷ 8 = ________

   Use your estimate to check if your answer is reasonable.

$$8\overline{)7,809}$$

−
______

−
______

−
______

On the Back!

6. Estimate first. Then choose a strategy to find the quotient for 4,816 ÷ 6.

Name ____________________

Build Mathematical Literacy
5-9

Read the problem. Then circle True or False for each statement. For each statement that is false, explain why using details from the text, if possible.

Construct Arguments Without dividing, how can you tell if the quotient for 5,873 ÷ 8 is greater than 700? Explain whether the quotient is less than 800.

1. A quotient is the answer to a division problem. True False

2. The problem asks you to divide to find the quotient for 5,873 ÷ 8. True False

3. You can multiply 8 × 700 to help you decide whether or not 5,873 ÷ 8 is greater than 700. True False

4. The product 8 × 700 also can help you decide whether or not 5,873 ÷ 8 is less than 800. True False

5. The solution to the problem will be a numerical answer. True False

Name ______________________________

Is the Bridge Safe?

The Davis Construction Company follows certain rules for building safe bridges: The distance between the bridge's supports, called the span, must not be more than 100 ft. The chart at the right shows how to classify bridges as very safe, safe, or unsafe. Find the span length of each bridge below. Then tell whether the bridge is very safe, safe, or unsafe.

Bridge Safety Ratings

Length of Span	Rating
0 to 50 ft	very safe
51 to 100 ft	safe
101 ft or more	unsafe

1. ngth of bridge: 252 ft

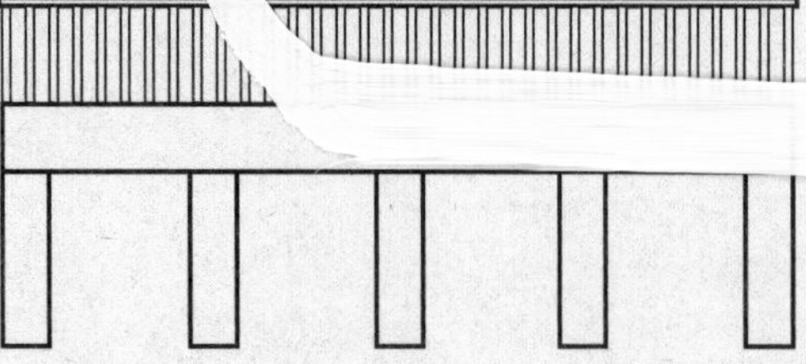

____

2. Length of bridge: 336 ft

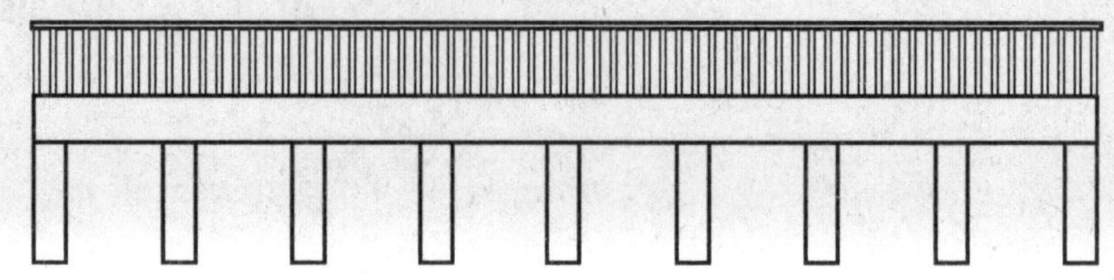

____

3. Length of bridge: 266 ft

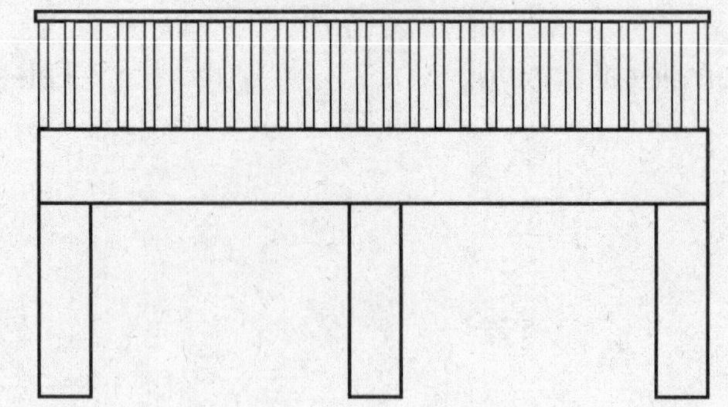

____

Name ______________________

Daily Review

5-10

1. What is the missing dividend in the equation?

$\square \div 8 = 60$

Ⓐ 48
Ⓑ 480
Ⓒ 4,800
Ⓓ 48,000

2. It costs $24 for admission to an amusement park. How much will it cost a group of 15 people to go to the amusement park?

Ⓐ $39
Ⓑ $120
Ⓒ $350
Ⓓ $360

3. Which shows 582,648 rounded to the nearest ten thousand?

Ⓐ 583,000
Ⓑ 580,000
Ⓒ 590,000
Ⓓ 600,000

4. Select all the statements with correctly estimated quotients.

- ☐ $3,105 \div 8$ is about 400.
- ☐ $2,462 \div 5$ is about 300.
- ☐ $234 \div 4$ is about 600.
- ☐ $4,318 \div 6$ is about 700.
- ☐ $5,472 \div 9$ is about 600.

5. Rachel has read 166 pages of a book with 310 pages. How many pages does Rachel need to read each day if she wants to finish the book in 6 days? Explain.

____

____

____

____

____

6. The Jones family spends $175 each month for their cell phone plan. How much does the family spend in 3 months?

____

7. Luke used counters to model a division problem. His work is shown below. What division problem did Luke model?

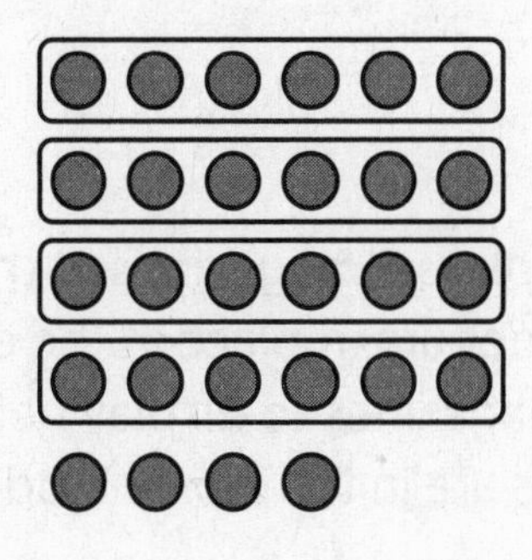

____

Name ______________________________

Reteach to Build Understanding
5-10

Vocabulary

1. A **variable** is a symbol or letter that stands for a number.

Write the addition equation represented by the bar diagram.

345	
123	*r*

____

Write the multiplication equation represented by the bar diagram.

t		
25	25	25

____

Sandra has 350 sheets of yellow paper and 420 sheets of pink paper. She is making math booklets. Each booklet uses 6 sheets of paper. How many booklets will Sandra be able to make with all the yellow and pink paper?

2. Complete the bar diagram to model the problem.

Write and solve an equation.

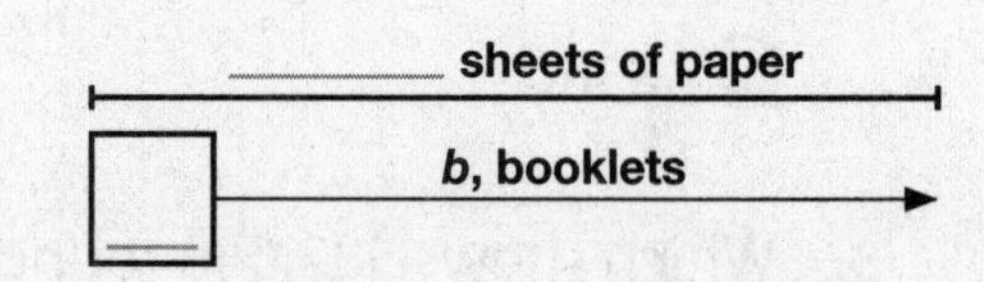

_______ + _______ $= p$

$p =$ _______ sheets of paper

3. Answer the original question: How many booklets can Sandra make?

_______ sheets of paper

b, booklets

Complete the bar diagram to model the problem.

Write and solve an equation.

_______ ÷ _______ $= b$

$b =$ _______

Sandra can make _______ booklets.

On the Back!

4. A store displays 5 magazines at the end of each aisle. A total of 22 magazines are in place at the end of all of the aisles. A stock person has 53 more magazines to display before each display is fully stocked. How many aisles are in the store? Model the math to solve the equation.

Name ______________________________

Read the problem. Answer the questions. Choose Yes or No to indicate whether you will need to use each of your answers to solve the problem.

Patricia and Antonio own a dog grooming business. To attract new customers, they offered free dog baths with the purchase of a grooming service. During the first 6 days of the promotion, they bathed 26 beagles, 12 boxers, 17 pugs, and 5 golden retrievers. Patricia and Antonio each bathed the same number of dogs each day. Draw a bar diagram. Write and solve an equation to find how many dogs, *d*, were bathed by Patricia.

Grooming Services
Nail Trim $4
Teeth Brushing $7
Ears Cleaned $5
Flea Treatment $5

1. Who owns the dog grooming business?

____

Will you use this information to solve the problem? Yes No

2. What is the special promotion that the business is offering?

____

Will you use this information to solve the problem? Yes No

3. What breeds did the owners bathe during the first 6 days of the promotion?

____

Will you use this information to solve the problem? Yes No

4. How many dogs were bathed during the first 6 days of the promotion?

____

Will you use this information to solve the problem? Yes No

5. How did Patricia and Antonio split the task of bathing the dogs?

____

Will you use this information to solve the problem? Yes No

Name ____________________

Enrichment

5-10

Up and Up!

Begin at the bottom of each ladder and solve each division problem to get to the top. If the problem has no remainder, climb two problems up. If the problem has a remainder, go down one problem.

Ladder 1

Finish!

$3\overline{)411}$

$7\overline{)877}$

$3\overline{)360}$

$8\overline{)896}$

$3\overline{)35}$

$4\overline{)588}$

$5\overline{)525}$

Ladder 2

Finish!

$7\overline{)794}$

$3\overline{)358}$

$5\overline{)575}$

$6\overline{)675}$

$7\overline{)786}$

$2\overline{)335}$

$6\overline{)72}$

Explain any difficulty you noticed in getting to the finish from Ladder 2.

____

____

____

____

Name ______________________

Use Operations with Whole Numbers to Solve Problems

Dear Family,

Your child is applying multiplication and division strategies to problem situations and exploring ways to find solutions.

This topic focuses on solving comparison problems as well as using addition, subtraction, multiplication, and division to solve multi-step problems. Your child will practice using the four operations to explore the relationship between separate values. Here is an activity you can try together.

Step by Step

Materials paper and pencil

Create and solve multi-step problems with your child. One person creates the first step of the problem. For example: This week Tom ran 2 miles one day and 3 miles another day. Next, the other person uses a different operation to construct the next step: Last week Tom ran 3 times farther than this week. How far did Tom run in two weeks? The first person then explains how to solve the problem: Tom ran $2 + 3 = 5$ miles this week. He ran $5 \times 3 = 15$ miles the week before, so he ran $5 + 15 = 20$ miles in two weeks. Vary the operations used and increase the number of steps as fluency allows.

Observe Your Child

Discuss different strategies for solving the same problem. Provide mathematical reasoning to support why the strategies would or would not work.

Nombre ______________________________

Usar operaciones con números enteros para resolver problemas

Estimada familia:

Su niño(a) está aplicando estrategias de multiplicación y división a situaciones o problemas y está explorando maneras de hallar soluciones.

Este tema se enfoca en la resolución de problemas de comparación y en el uso de la suma, la resta, la multiplicación y la división para resolver problemas de varios pasos. Su niño(a) practicará cómo usar las cuatro operaciones para explorar la relación entre valores diferentes. Pruebe esta actividad con su niño(a).

Paso a paso

Materiales papel y lápiz

Cree y resuelva un problema de varios pasos con su niño(a). Una persona crea el primer paso del problema. Por ejemplo: Esta semana, Tom corrió 2 millas un día y 3 millas otro día. Después, la otra persona usa otra operación para construir el siguiente paso: La semana pasada, Tom corrió 3 veces la distancia que corrió esta semana. ¿Qué distancia corrió Tom en las dos semanas? Luego, la primera persona explica cómo resolver el problema: Tom corrió $2 + 3 = 5$ millas esta semana. Corrió $5 \times 3 = 15$ millas la semana anterior; por tanto, corrió $5 + 15 = 20$ millas en las dos semanas. Varíen las operaciones usadas y aumenten la cantidad de pasos en la medida en que la fluidez lo permita.

Observe a su niño(a)

Comenten distintas estrategias para resolver el mismo problema. Utilicen el razonamiento matemático para explicar por qué las estrategias podrían funcionar o no.

Name ______________________________

Pick a Project

Project 6A

Giant Redwood Trees

Look up. Higher. Keep looking. You'll have to look very high to see the tops of the Coastal Redwood trees. They are the tallest trees on Earth. Some trees are over 350 feet tall. That is taller than the Statue of Liberty! As the trees grow, they also become wider. Some trees are 20 feet across.

Coastal Redwoods are also some of the oldest trees on Earth. The oldest known redwood tree is over 2,000 years old. These trees need a lot of water. They grow well along the Pacific coast of the United States where the air is often moist with fog. Some of the tallest trees grow in Redwood National Park in California, but they are found all along the coast.

Your Project Model the Height of a Redwood Tree

The tallest known coastal redwood is named Hyperion. It is 380 feet tall. Plan how you could model this tree using paper clips. Decide what length each paper clip represents. For example, 1 paper clip = 10 feet. On a sheet of poster paper, use the paper clips to model the height of the tree. Glue or tape them in place. Include a key. Write a multiplication statement to describe the model.

Then, work with an adult to research several other tall objects, such as buildings or statues. Use paper clips to model their heights and add them to the poster paper. Label them. Then, compare their heights to that of Hyperion. Write a two-step problem to compare at least two heights. Share your problem and its solution with the class.

Name ______________________________

Pick a Project

Project 6B

Manatee

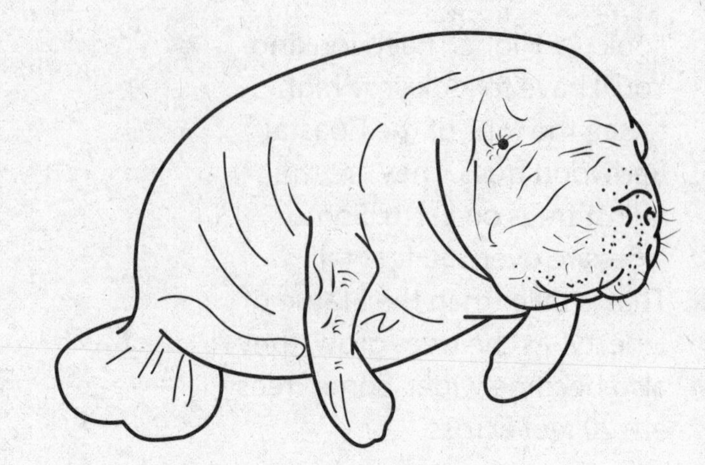

Imagine seeing a large, gray animal swimming slowly through shallow waters. Its large, flat tail might make it look like a mermaid, but it is a manatee. Although they are sometimes known as sea cows, manatees are actually related to elephants.

In the 1970s, the number of manatees had become so low that scientists feared they would disappear from Earth. There were just a few hundred left. Wildlife organizations worked to protect them. Once endangered, the manatee is now listed as threatened.

Cold temperatures and hurricanes can harm manatees. But people are the biggest threat to them. Manatees are hurt or killed every year by boats and other watercraft. They are also harmed by trash and chemicals that people add to water. Everyone needs to do their part to make sure manatees are here for a long time to come.

Your Project Make a Presentation with Manatee Number Facts

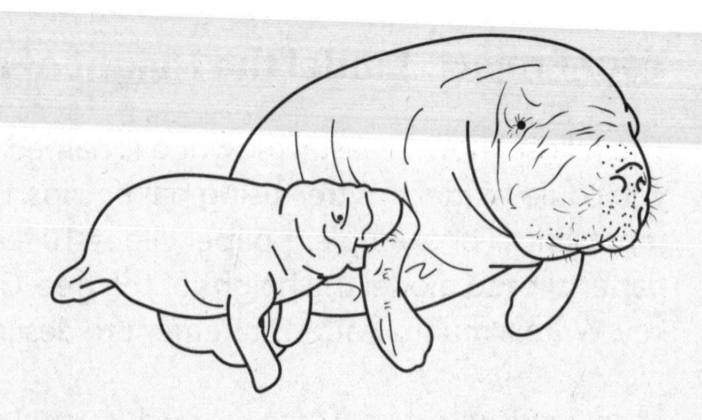

Research manatee. Collect some facts with numbers, such as the average weight of a newborn or adult manatee, their average lengths, or how fast they swim.

Develop a presentation about your facts, and create 1 or 2 two-step math problems that use the number facts in your presentation. Present your facts to the class, and have them answer your problems.

Create a poster to show the number facts you found, and write 1 or 2 math problems that use the number facts.

Name ___________________________

Pick a Project

Project 6C

American Alligator

What animal has a mouthful of large teeth, is covered by a thick skin, and can grow more than 14 feet long and over 1,000 pounds? It's the American Alligator. Freshwater ponds, rivers, and marshes throughout the southeastern United States are home to millions of alligators. These fearless animals get around by swimming, but they can also walk, crawl, and run on land.

The number of alligators became very low in the 1950s. They had been hunted and their habitats were being destroyed. Alligators were in danger of disappearing forever. Several wildlife agencies worked together to protect alligators, and now they are no longer considered to be in danger.

Your Project Compare Numbers of Alligators

Alligators produce young in eggs. Temperature determines whether the newborn alligators will be males or females. The table describes 100 alligator babies born from eggs kept at different temperatures.

Temperature (C)	Number of Females	Number of Males
28	100	0
31	75	25
33	30	70
35	0	100

Make a bar diagram to compare the numbers of males and females at each temperature. Write a caption to explain how temperature affects alligator babies. Share your diagram with the class.

Name ______________________________________

Pick a Project

Project 6D

Loggerhead Sea Turtle

The loggerhead sea turtle, sometimes just called a loggerhead, is named for its large head. Its large head supports its incredibly powerful jaws. The skin of a loggerhead is usually yellow or brown, while its shell is a reddish brown. Loggerheads can be found throughout the world, in different oceans and seas. These turtles eat both animals and plants and generally live to be about 45 to 65 years old.

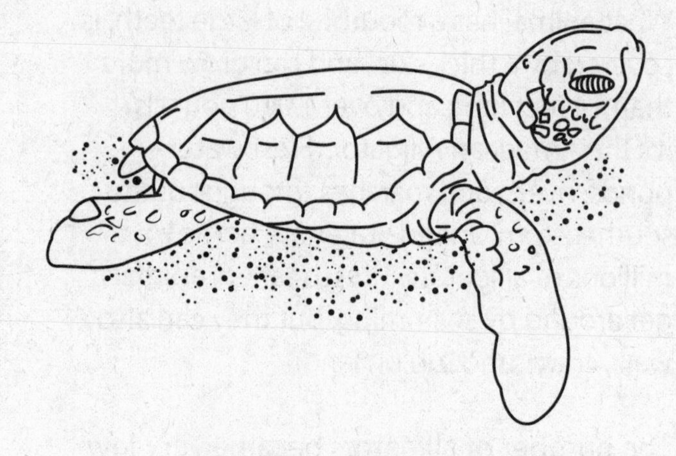

Loggerheads are the largest kind of hard-shelled turtles. On average, loggerheads are about 3 feet long and weigh about 300 pounds. But some large loggerheads can weigh over 1,000 pounds.

Your Project Find the Number of Turtle Eggs

When a loggerhead turtle is ready to lay eggs, she travels to a beach. There she digs a hole, or nest, for the eggs. Each egg is soft and flexible so it does not break as it drops in the hole. Make a model of a turtle egg. You can show your model egg in a nest.

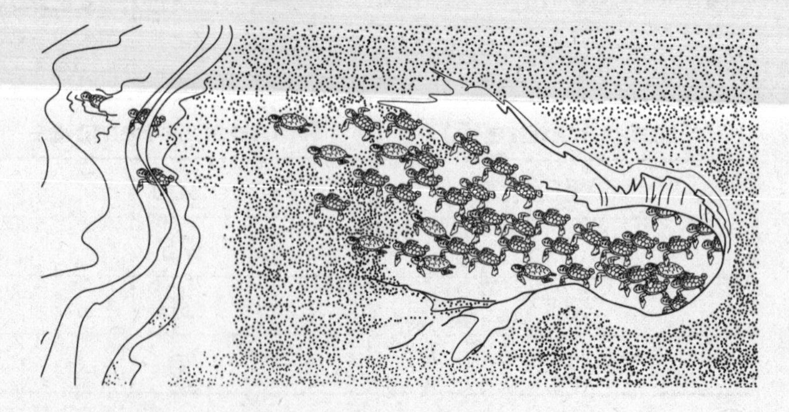

Suppose a loggerhead turtle makes 4 nests in one season. She lays an average of 109 eggs in each nest. Write an equation to find how many eggs she laid this season, and then solve. Attach your equation and solution to your model.

Name ______________________________

A Breath of Fresh Air!

Did You Know? For every gallon of gas a car uses, 20 pounds of carbon dioxide (CO_2) are released into the atmosphere. Typical cars have gas-only engines. Hybrid cars, however, run on a combination of rechargeable batteries and gas. The battery power reduces the amount of pollution typically generated by a car. In addition to reducing air pollution, hybrid cars are very quiet, which reduces noise pollution as well.

1 Hybrid cars get very good gas mileage, which means less money is spent on gas. Four different hybrid cars are represented in the table. Use multiplication or division to complete the table. Draw bar diagrams if needed.

Hybrid Car Comparison

Car	Gas Tank Size (gallons)	Average Highway Miles per Gallon	Gallons of Gas Used	Total Miles Traveled
A	16	47	9	423
B	17	45	25	
C	11	43	18	
D	13		7	280

2 Car A begins with a full tank of gas. How many more miles can the car travel before the gas tank is empty? Explain how you solve. Use one or more equations in your explanation. Tell what your variables represent.

____

____

3 **Extension** A typical car uses 16 gallons of gas to travel 400 miles. Car D uses 10 gallons of gas to travel the same distance. How many fewer pounds of carbon dioxide are released into the atmosphere by driving 400 miles in Car D instead of driving a typical car the same distance? Explain how you solve. Use one or more equations in your explanation. Tell what your variables represent.

____

____

Name ______________________

enVision® STEM Activity 6-6

Solar Panels

Did You Know? Solar panels convert the sun's energy directly into electricity using semiconductors, such as silicon. The amount of electricity produced depends on the amount of sunlight hitting the panel, the size of the panel, and the efficiency of the solar cells inside the panel. On average, a typical solar panel produces about 200 watts of power.

In order to reduce electricity costs, a homeowner has 9 solar panels installed on his roof. Each solar panel produces 235 watts of power.

1. How much power do the solar panels produce in all?

____

2. Of the 9 solar panels, 2 are not working properly. A technician removed the broken panels. How much power do the remaining solar panels produce in all?

   What is the hidden question?

   ____

   Write and solve an equation to answer the hidden question.

   ____

   Write and solve an equation to answer the original question.

   ____

3. While the broken panels are being repaired, the technician installed 8 new smaller solar panels that produce 158 watts of power each. How much power do all the current solar panels produce? Explain.

____

4. **Extension** Another house on the block installed 15 mini panels that each produce 55 watts of power and 15 mini panels that each produce 60 watts of power. How much power is produced by all the mini panels? Explain.

____

____

Name ______________________________

Daily Review

6-1

1. A store employee counts 285 different lawn decorations. He wants to organize them and place the lawn decorations on 9 shelves. About how many lawn decorations will go on each shelf?

Ⓐ About 30 decorations

Ⓑ About 40 decorations

Ⓒ About 50 decorations

Ⓓ About 90 decorations

2. Polk County, Florida has an area of 1,798 square miles. The neighboring county of Osceola has an area of 1,327 square miles. What is the total area of these two counties combined?

Ⓐ 3,025 square milles

Ⓑ 3,115 square milles

Ⓒ 3,125 square milles

Ⓓ 3,225 square milles

3. Raja put 35 marbles into each jar. There are 28 jars. How many marbles did Raja put into all the jars?

Ⓐ 980 marbles

Ⓑ 840 marbles

Ⓒ 340 marbles

Ⓓ 63 marbles

4. Which comparison is true?

Ⓐ $82{,}429 > 83{,}932$

Ⓑ $69{,}492 > 69{,}742$

Ⓒ $45{,}920 < 45{,}936$

Ⓓ $23{,}950 < 21{,}492$

5. Dennis has 171 shells in his collection. Fred has 208 shells. Round each amount to the nearest ten. About how many more shells does Fred have?

____

6. Mandy said $7{,}848 + 52{,}439 = 60{,}277$. Is Mandy's sum reasonable?

____

____

7. Ian multiplies a number by 5. The product of the two numbers is 495. What number does Ian multiply by 5? Explain.

____

____

____

____

____

____

8. Bryce grows a sunflower that contains 1,354 sunflower seeds. Six people share the harvested seeds. If they share the seeds equally, how many seeds will be left over?

____

Name ___________________________

Vocabulary

1. You can write an **equation** to solve comparison problems. An equation is a number sentence that uses the equal sign (=) to show that two expressions have the same value. Phrases, such as *times as many as* or *more than*, can be used to compare quantities.

Compare with Multiplication
There are 6 toys and 3 times as many books. How many books, *b*, are there?

Compare with Addition
There are 6 toys. There are 12 more books than toys. How many books are there?

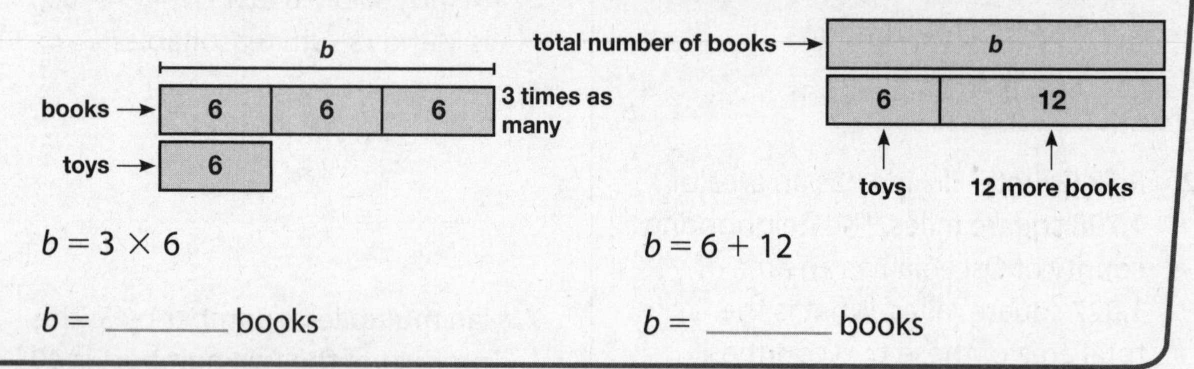

$b = 3 \times 6$

$b =$ _______ books

$b = 6 + 12$

$b =$ _______ books

2. **Compare with Multiplication**
Malli has 8 times as many crayons as Morgan. Morgan has 16 crayons. How many crayons, *c*, does Malli have?

Find _______ times as many as _______.

$c = 8 \times 16$ $\quad c =$ _______ crayons

3. **Compare with Addition**
Brady has 163 baseball cards. Sammy has 256 more baseball cards than Brady. How many baseball cards, *b*, does Sammy have?

Find _______ more than _______.

$b = 256 + 163$ $\quad b =$ _______ baseball cards

On the Back!

4. Decide whether to compare with multiplication or addition. Write a comparison sentence for the problem below. Then write and solve an equation.

Mariah took 76 pictures on vacation. Her sister took 29 more pictures than she did. How many pictures did Mariah's sister take?

Name ______________________

Build Mathematical Literacy
6-1

Read the problem. Answer each question to help understand the problem. Then, tell whether the information used to answer the question was directly stated in the text (DS), implied in the text (I), or based only on previous knowledge (PK).

A shirt is on sale for *d* dollars. The regular price is 4 times as much. Todd has enough money to buy 2 shirts at the regular price. How many shirts can Todd buy at the sale price? Explain.

1. What does *d* represent?

____

2. How many shirts can Todd buy at the regular price?

____

3. Will Todd be able to buy more or fewer shirts at the sale price than the regular price?

____

4. What is the relationship between the regular price of the shirt and the sale price of the shirt?

____

5. If you knew the regular price of the shirt, how could you use that information to find the sale price of the shirt?

____

____

6. What exactly is the question asking you to find?

____

Name ______________________________

Recess Time!

Use the following clues to complete the table. Write an equation you can use to find the number of minutes of recess each grade gets each day.

- The fifth grade class gets 15 minutes of recess each day.
- The fourth grade class gets 10 more minutes of recess than the fifth grade class.
- The third grade class gets twice as many minutes of recess as the fifth grade class.
- The second grade class gets 15 more minutes of recess than the fourth grade class.
- The first grade class gets 3 times as many minutes of recess as the fifth grade class.
- The kindergarten class gets 30 more minutes of recess than the fourth grade class.

Grade	Equation	Minutes of Recess
5		15
4	$f =$	
3	$t =$	
2	$s =$	
1	$r =$	
K	$k =$	

Name ___________________________

Daily Review

6-2

1. Alexandra has 127 flowers. She puts the same number of flowers in each of her vases. How many flowers will be left over?

Ⓐ 3 flowers

Ⓑ 4 flowers

Ⓒ 8 flowers

Ⓓ 12 flowers

2. Look at the model below. Which expression best describes the model?

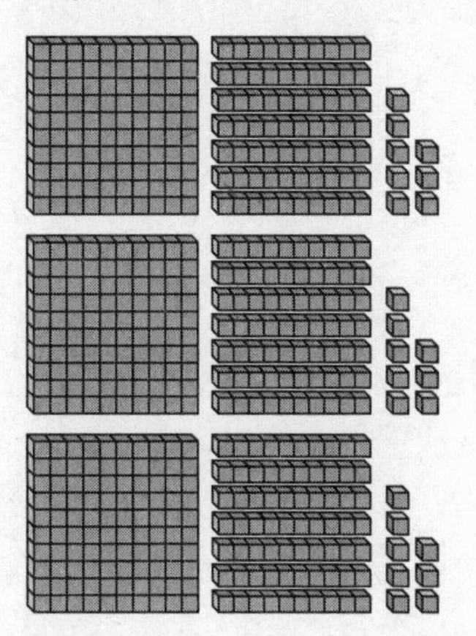

Ⓐ $3 + (100 + 70 + 8)$

Ⓑ $3 \times (100 + 70 + 8)$

Ⓒ $3 \times (100 \times 70 \times 8)$

Ⓓ $(100 + 70 + 8) \div 3$

3. Keith planted 15 rows of carrots. Each row had 35 carrot plants. How many carrots did Keith plant?

____

4. Jackson wants to buy a pair of sneakers that cost $106. So far, he has saved $57. How much more does Jackson have to save to buy the sneakers?

____

5. Write 621,840 in expanded form.

____

____

6. Write a number in which the value of the digit in the ten-thousands place is ten times as great as the value of the digit in the thousands place.

____

7. How many eggs are in 12 dozen?

____

8. There are 13 items in a baker's dozen. If Natalie orders 9 baker's dozen of muffins, how many muffins did Natalie order?

____

Name ______________________________

Vocabulary

1. Multiplication and division are operations that have an inverse relationship. **Inverse operations** are operations that undo each other.

$4 \times 6 = 24$ $\qquad$ $5 \times 5 =$ ______ $\qquad$ $3 \times 7 =$ ______

$24 \div 6 = 4$ $\qquad$ ______ $\div 5 = 5$ $\qquad$ ______ $\div 7 = 3$

2. Cole has 4 eggs. Ava has 48 eggs. How many times as many eggs does Ava have as Cole?

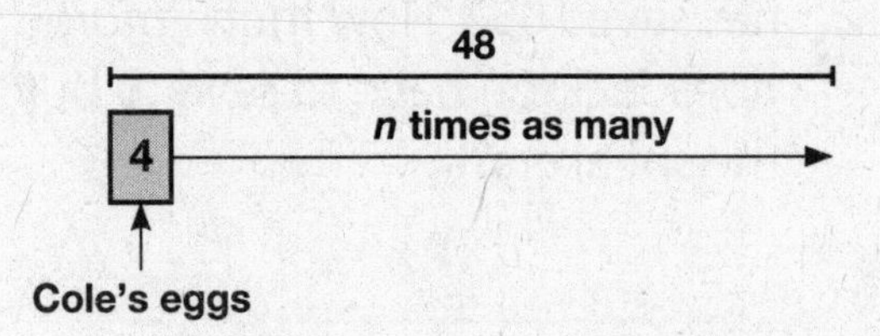

Write a multiplication equation to compare the number of eggs.

Ava's eggs = n × Cole's eggs

$48 = n \times 4$

Since you know the original amount and the total, divide to find how many times as many.

If $48 = n \times 4$, then $n = 48 \div 4$.

$n =$ ______

Ava has ______ times as many eggs as Cole.

3. Carly ran 3 times as far as Dani last month. Dani ran 32 miles. How many miles, m, did Carly run?

3 ______________________ 32 is m.

$m =$ ______ × ______

$m =$ ______

Carly ran ______ miles.

On the Back!

4. Zoe picked 5 times as many pints of strawberries as Heidi. Heidi picked 16 pints of strawberries. How many pints, p, did Zoe pick?

Name ____________________

Build Mathematical Literacy
6-2

Read the problem. Then, read each sentence individually. Identify what you know and what you need to know after reading each sentence.

Miranda has 4 times as many leaves in her collection as Joy. Joy has 13 more leaves than Armani. Armani has 10 leaves in his collection. How many leaves does Miranda have in her collection? Explain.

Miranda has 4 times as many leaves in her collection as Joy.

1. What do you know that you can use to solve the problem?

2. What do you still need to know to solve the problem?

Joy has 13 more leaves than Armani.

3. What do you know that can be used to solve the problem?

4. What do you still need to know to solve the problem?

Armani has 10 leaves in his collection.

5. What do you know that you can use to solve the problem?

6. What do you still need to know to solve the problem?

Name ______________________

Enrichment
6-2

Calendars for Charity

Five students sold calendars for charity. Use the clues below to find how many calendars they sold in all.

- April sold 14 calendars.
- Isabel sold 12 times as many calendars as April.
- Isabel sold twice as many calendars as Juan.
- Sydney sold 35 more calendars than Juan.
- Sydney sold 43 more calendars than Yuri.

Answer the questions below. Write an equation to explain how you answer each.

1. How many calendars, *i*, did Isabel sell?

____

2. How many calendars, *j*, did Juan sell?

____

3. How many calendars, *s*, did Sydney sell?

____

4. How many calendars, *y*, did Yuri sell?

____

5. How many calendars, *t*, did the five students sell in all?

____

____

Name ______________________________

Daily Review

6-3

1. Nick has \$20. He wants to buy as many toy cars as he can. Each car costs \$3. How many toy cars can Nick buy?

Ⓐ 6 toy cars
Ⓑ 7 toy cars
Ⓒ 17 toy cars
Ⓓ 23 toy cars

2. Round 394,294 to the nearest thousand.

Ⓐ 395,000
Ⓑ 394,000
Ⓒ 390,000
Ⓓ 380,000

3. Which statement best describes the equation below?

$24 = 4 \times 6$

Ⓐ 24 is 4 less than 6.
Ⓑ 24 is 4 greater than 6.
Ⓒ 24 is 6 times as many as 6.
Ⓓ 24 is 4 times as many as 6.

4. Find the product of 83×56.

Ⓐ 903
Ⓑ 4,638
Ⓒ 4,648
Ⓓ 5,295

5. Select all the expressions that correctly show how to use mental math to find the product of 4×321.

☐ $4 \times (300 + 20 + 1)$
☐ $4 + (300 \times 20 \times 1)$
☐ $4 \times (300 \times 20 \times 1)$
☐ $(4 \times 300) + (4 \times 20) + (4 \times 1)$
☐ $(4 + 300) + (4 + 20) + (4 + 1)$

6. Gabriella collected 68 trading cards. She shared them equally among 4 friends. How many cards did she give each of her friends?

____

7. Harry guesses there are 7,758 beans in a jar. His guess is 3 times the actual number of beans. Complete the bar diagram. Write and solve an equation to find the actual number of beans in the jar.

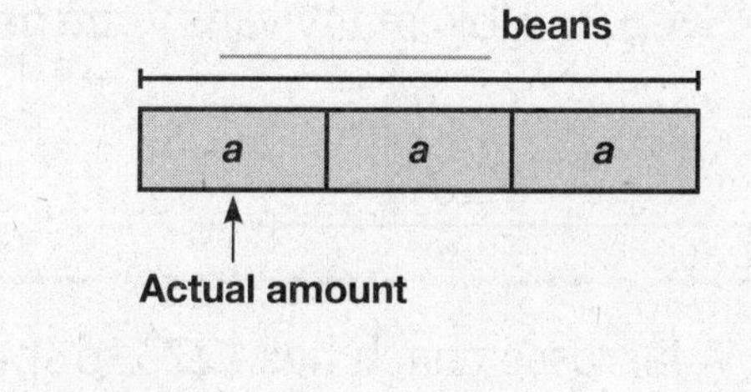

____

____

8. Find the difference $100{,}467 - 87{,}275$.

____

9. A company has \$3,500 to spend on amusement park tickets. Each ticket costs \$9. What is the greatest number of tickets the company can buy?

____

Name ____________________

Reteach to Build Understanding
6-3

Vocabulary

1. When you solve multi-step problems, it can be helpful to write an **equation** for each step. Equations use an equal sign (=) to show that two expressions have the same value.

There are 96 students on a field trip. The boys and girls ride in separate vans. 8 students ride in each van. The boys fill 4 vans. How many vans do the girls need?

Step 1: How many boys b, are on the field trip?
$4 \times 8 = b$

$b =$ ________ boys

b
| 8 | 8 | 8 | 8 |

Step 2: How many girls g, are on the field trip?
$96 - 32 = g$

$g =$ ________ girls

96
| ___ | g |
Number of boys

Step 3: How many vans v, are needed for the girls?
$v = 64 \div 8$

$v =$ ________ vans

___ girls
8 → v times

2. A lacrosse coach has $275 to spend on equipment. He buys 3 goals for $75 each. Mouth guards cost $5 each. How many mouth guards can the coach buy?

Step 1: How many dollars d, did the coach spend on goals?

$d =$ ________ goals × ________ each

$d =$ ________

d
| ___ | ___ | ___ |

Step 2: How much money m, is left?

$m =$ ________ − ________

$m =$ ________

___
| ___ | m |

Step 3: How many mouth guards g, can the coach buy?

$g =$ ________ ÷ ________

$g =$ ________ mouth guards

On the Back!

3. On Saturday, a bakery sold 6 cakes and several cupcakes. The bakery made a total of $165. If cakes sell for $12 each, and cupcakes sell for $3 each, how many cupcakes did they sell?

Name ______________________________

Build Mathematical Literacy
6-3

Read the problem. Mark the correct column to show whether the answer to the question can be found in the problem text, the image, or by answering a hidden question.

Model with Math A power plant has 4 tons of coal. A ton of coal produces 2,460 kilowatt hours of electricity. The plant reserves enough electricity to power 9 light bulbs for a year. How many additional kilowatt hours of electricity are produced? Draw bar diagrams and write one or more equations to show how you solve. Tell what your variables represent.

It takes 876 kilowatt hours of electricity to power a 100-watt light bulb for a year.

Question	Text	Image	Hidden Question
1. How many kilowatt hours of electricity does it take to power 9 light bulbs for a year?			
2. How many kilowatts hours of electricity does a ton of coal produce?			
3. How many kilowatt hours of electricity does it take to power a 100-watt light bulb for a year?			
4. How many kilowatt hours of electricity can the power plant produce with the coal they have?			
5. How much coal does the power plant have?			

Name ______________________

Enrichment
6-3

Colorful Arena

A professional basketball arena seats 17,098 people. The team owners give away souvenirs by putting them on seats before the game. One night they put red t-shirts in 8 sections which seat 950 people each. They put blue t-shirts in 6 sections which seat 975 people each. Finally, they put red and blue caps on the seats of the remaining 4 sections. How many people got caps?

1. Use the bar diagram and one or more equations to show how you solve.

C = the number of people who got caps.

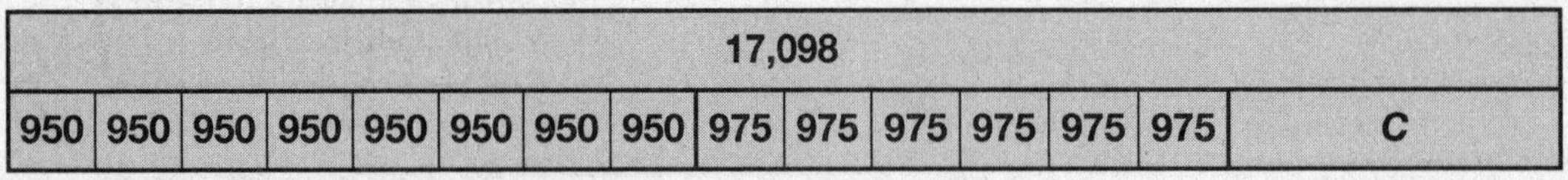

17,098														
950	950	950	950	950	950	950	950	975	975	975	975	975	975	C

2. Explain how to use an estimate to show that your answer is reasonable.

3. How many people sit in each of the sections which got caps? Write an equation to show how you solve. Tell what your variable represents.

Name ______________________

Daily Review
6-4

1. What is 648,923 rounded to the nearest ten thousand?

Ⓐ 640,000
Ⓑ 648,000
Ⓒ 649,000
Ⓓ 650,000

2. In a recent year, the population of Pittsburgh was three hundred five thousand, seven hundred four people. What is this number in standard form?

Ⓐ 350,841
Ⓑ 305,740
Ⓒ 305,704
Ⓓ 305,470

3. A passenger train has 82 cars. Five cars can hold 32 passengers. Two cars are for dining and no tickets are sold for that car. The remaining cars can hold 48 passengers. How many passengers can ride on the train?

Ⓐ 3,600 passengers
Ⓑ 3,760 passengers
Ⓒ 3,840 passengers
Ⓓ 3,936 passengers

4. Marjorie's school has 8 buses to go on the field trip. Each bus will hold the same number of students. There are 224 students going on the field trip. How many students will ride in each bus?

Ⓐ 28 students
Ⓑ 32 students
Ⓒ 35 students
Ⓓ 38 students

The table shows the number of bagels sold on Friday at 3 locations of the Bagel Shop. Use the table to answer **5** and **6**.

Friday's Sales at The Bagel Shop

Store Location	Bagels Sold
West Lake	67
Downtown	90
Bay Harbor	149

5. The West Lake location sells bagels for $6 each. About how much money do they make on the Friday? Explain how you estimate.

____

____

____

6. The Bay Harbor location prepares the same number of bagels they sold on Friday for the next Friday. They store them in boxes which each hold 9 bagels. How many boxes do they need? Explain.

____

____

____

____

____

____

Name ______________________

Vocabulary

An **expression** contains numbers and at least one operation. It can also contain letters which stand for numbers, called variables. Expressions do not have an equal sign (=). When you solve a multi-step problem, you can use expressions to represent the answers to hidden questions. Then, you can combine your expressions into an equation.

1. Is $4 \times (w + 9)$ an expression or an equation? ______________

2. Is $w = 4 \times (3 + 9)$ an expression or an equation? ______________

3. Li Marie is setting up water stations for a 5-kilometer race. She has 9 water tables. She buys 24 packages of cups with 12 cups in each package. She wants to put the same number of cups on each table. How many cups should she put on each table?

Step 1: Write an expression to represent the total number of cups Li Marie buys.

12	24 times →

____

Step 2: Complete the equation to find t, the number of cups Li Marie should put on each table. Include the expression you wrote in Step 1.

$t =$ (________ × ________) ÷ ________

12	24 times →							
t	*t*	*t*	*t*	*t*	*t*	*t*	*t*	*t*

Step 3: Solve.

Li Marie should put ________ cups on each table.

On the Back!

4. Li Marie's water tables are evenly spaced along the 5,000-meter (or 5-kilometer) course, including one at the beginning and one at the end. What is the distance between each pair of tables that are next to each other? Hint: There are not 9 sections between tables.

Name ______________________

Build Mathematical Literacy
6-4

Read the problem. Then, circle *True* or *False* for each statement.
For each statement that is false, explain why, using details from the text, if possible.

Kendra is using 27 blue patches and some white patches to make a quilt. The quilt has a total area of 540 square inches. Each patch has an area of 9 square inches. How much of the area of the quilt is white?

1. The quilt has a length of 540 inches. True False

2. The length of a side of the blue square is 9 inches. True False

3. The expression $540 \div 9$ represents the total number of squares in the quilt. True False

4. The problem is solved by finding the product of the lengths of two sides of the quilt. True False

5. The expression 9×27 is the area of the white squares. True False

Name ________________________

Racing Pool

Use the diagram of the swimming pool to solve the following problem.

Elsa swims 4 laps of backstroke for a race. A lap is down and back. How far does she swim in all, not including the turns?

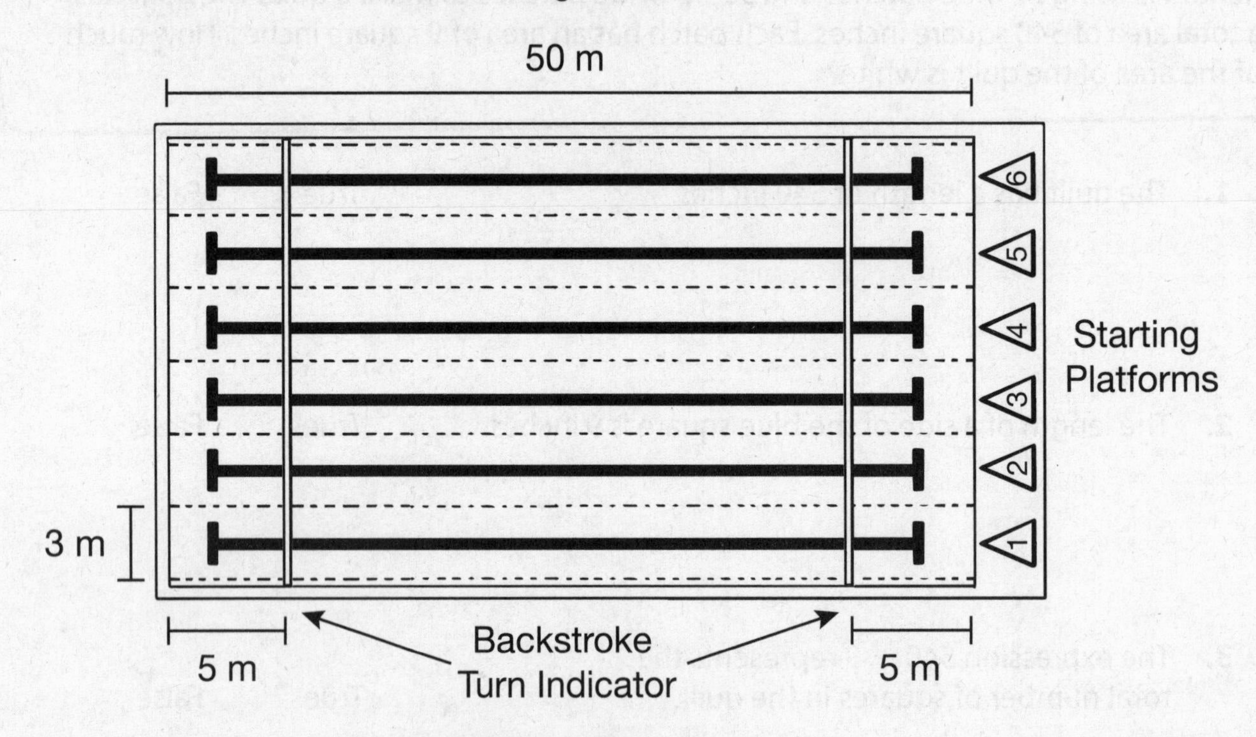

1. Write one or more equations to show one way to solve the problem. Tell what your variables represent.

2. Write one or more equations to show another way to solve the problem. Tell what your variables represent.

Name ______________________

Daily Review

6-5

1. Jordi's mother earned $36,295 last year. His father earned $29,472. How much did they earn in all?

Ⓐ $55,667

Ⓑ $65,667

Ⓒ $65,767

Ⓓ $66,667

2. Donna has read 9 chapters in her book. The book has 12 chapters in all. Each chapter has 38 pages. How many more pages does Donna have to read to finish the book?

Ⓐ 1,194 pages Ⓒ 114 pages

Ⓑ 456 pages Ⓓ 76 pages

3. Select all the correct comparisons.

☐ 246,348 > 246,438

☐ 185,295 < 185,306

☐ 568,400 < 559,412

☐ 375,120 > 372,897

☐ 606,660 = 606,660

4. Write 35,806 in expanded form.

____

5. Kaylee drew the array below to show a division sentence. What division sentence did Kaylee show?

□□□□□□
□□□□□□
□□□□□□

____

6. Guitar lessons cost $25 an hour. Last month, Sam had 5 hours of lessons one week and 4 hours each of the other 3 weeks. What was the total cost for the month? Write equations to solve. Tell what your variables represent.

____

____

____

____

____

____

7. The parking lot for the high school football stadium has 83 rows, with 19 parking spaces in each row. The lot for the baseball stadium has 68 rows with 14 parking spaces in each row. About how many more cars can park at the football stadium than the baseball stadium? Explain.

____

____

____

____

____

____

Name ____________________

Vocabulary

1. A **variable** is a symbol or letter that stands for a number. When solving multi-step problems, you can use variables to represent unknown quantities.

   Amelia traveled 57 miles by car on her vacation. Gina traveled 7 times as many miles as Amelia on her vacation. What is the difference between the distance Amelia traveled and the distance Gina traveled?

   Step 1 Determine the hidden question. Write and solve an equation using a variable for the unknown.
   Hidden Question: How many miles did Gina travel for vacation?
   Let g, represent the miles Gina traveled.
   $7 \times 57 = g$

   $g =$ ______ miles

   Step 2 Use the answer to the hidden question to answer the original question.
   Original Question: What is the difference between the distance Amelia traveled and the distance Gina traveled? Let $d =$ the difference in the miles they traveled.

   ______ $- 57 = d$

   $d =$ ______ miles

2. Ms. Po served a total of 30 years in Congress. A term is 6 years in the Senate and 2 years in the House of Representatives. She served 3 terms in the Senate. How many terms did she serve in the House of Representatives?

   Step 1 Find s, the years Ms. Po served in the Senate.

   $s =$ ______ terms $\times$ ______ years per term, $s =$ ______ years

   Step 2 Find h, the years she served in the House of Representatives.

   $h =$ ______ years $-$ ______ years, $h =$ ______ years

   Step 3 Find t, the terms she served in the House of Representatives.

   $t =$ ______ years $\div$ ______ years per term, $t =$ ______ terms

On the Back!

3. Twelve student tickets and 3 adult tickets cost $96. The student tickets cost $6 each. What is the cost of an adult ticket?

Name ______________________________

Build Mathematical Literacy
6-5

Read the problem. Then, read each part individually. Identify what you know and what you need to know after reading each part.

Model with Math Anna earns $8 an hour baby-sitting and $6 an hour working in the garden. Last month, she worked 15 hours baby-sitting and 8 hours in the garden. How much more money does she need to buy a robot which costs $199? Explain how you solve. Use one or more equations in your explanation. Tell what your variables represent.

Anna earns $8 an hour baby-sitting and $6 an hour working in the garden. Last month, she worked 15 hours baby-sitting and 8 hours in the garden.

1. What can you use in the text above to answer the question: How much more money does she need to buy a robot that costs $199?

____

____

____

2. What do you still need to know to answer the question: How much more money does she need to buy a robot that costs $199?

____

____

How much more money does she need to buy a robot which costs $199?

3. What do you know that you can use to solve the problem?

____

4. What do you still need to know to solve the problem?

____

Name ______________________________

Car Wash Day

Solve each problem. Write and solve equations to answer each hidden question and the original question. Tell what each variable represents.

1. The school held a Car Wash Day. It ran from 10 A.M. to 4 P.M. The students washed 12 cars in the first hour, 15 cars in the second hour, and 10 cars in each of the remaining hours. They charged $8 a car. How much money did they earn in all?

____

____

____

____

____

____

2. Explain why your answer to Exercise 1 is reasonable.

____

____

____

3. During the first 2 hours, 12 students worked each hour. During the remaining hours, 15 students worked each hour. What was the total number of hours worked by all the students combined?

____

____

____

____

____

Name ___________________________

Daily Review
6-6

1. In which number is the value of the first 4 ten times as great as the value of the second 4?

Ⓐ 194,340
Ⓑ 348,450
Ⓒ 554,450
Ⓓ 404,040

2. Henry reads for 20 minutes each day. Alicia reads for 30 minutes each day. They both read 7 days a week. How many more minutes does Alicia read than Henry in 2 weeks?

Ⓐ 70 minutes
Ⓑ 140 minutes
Ⓒ 240 minutes
Ⓓ 350 minutes

3. Mr. Beasley needs to replace the windows in his house. Each new window costs \$186. How much will it cost to replace 8 windows?

Ⓐ \$848
Ⓑ \$1,116
Ⓒ \$1,288
Ⓓ \$1,488

4. Select all the expressions which show how to use mental math to find the product of 5×680.

☐ $5 \times (600 + 80)$
☐ $(5 \times 600) + (5 \times 8)$
☐ $(5 \times 600) + (5 \times 80)$
☐ $(5 \times 600) + (6 \times 80)$
☐ $(5 \times 700) - (5 \times 20)$

5. The cost of a season pass to the zoo is 3 times as much as a 1-day pass. The cost of a 1-day pass is \$12. Write and solve an equation to find the cost, *c*, of a season pass.

____

6. There are 42 people who have signed up for a bowling league. There will be 4 people on each team. How many full teams can be formed? Explain.

____
____
____
____

7. Use the area model to find 32×25. Write the partial products.

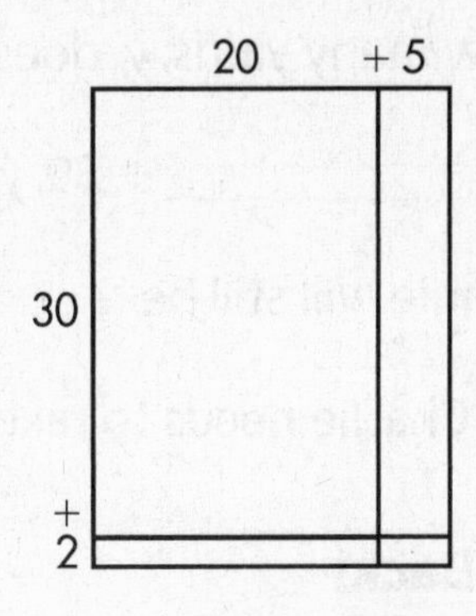

____
____

Name ________________________________

Reteach to Build Understanding
6-6

Vocabulary

1. A **remainder** is the number that remains after the division is complete. When solving problems, you may need to interpret the remainder to answer the question.

$30 \div 8 = a$ $56 \div 7 = h$ $16 \div 3 = p$

$a =$ ________ $h =$ ________ $p =$ ________

Elliott and Charlie need to buy running shoes. Elliott's shoes cost $38. Charlie's shoes cost 4 times as much as Elliott's shoes. Charlie made $67 from mowing lawns. He also makes $9 a yard for raking leaves. How many yards does Charlie need to rake to have enough money to buy his shoes?

2. Charlie's shoes cost 4 times as much as Elliott's shoes. Find, s, the cost of Charlie's shoes.

   $s = 4 \times \$38$, $s =$ ________

   Charlie's shoes cost ________.

   Use the cost of Charlie's shoes to find how much more money, m, Charlie needs to earn.

   ____________ $- \$67$, $m =$ ________

   Charlie needs to earn ________ more.

   How many yards, y, does Charlie need to rake?

   ____________ $\div \$9$, $y =$ ________

   Charlie will still be ________ short if he rakes ________ yards.

   So, Charlie needs to rake ________ yards.

On the Back!

3. The middle school golf team is selling golf balls to raise $850 for new equipment. They sell golf balls for $2 each. A pack has 6 golf balls. How many packs of golf balls does the team need to sell to raise enough money for new equipment?

Name ___________________________

Build Mathematical Literacy
6-6

Read the problem. Answer the questions to help understand how to solve the problem.

Rainey's group designed the flag shown for a class project. They used 234 square inches of green fabric. After making one flag, Rainey's group has 35 square inches of yellow fabric left. How can Rainey's group determine the total area of the flag?

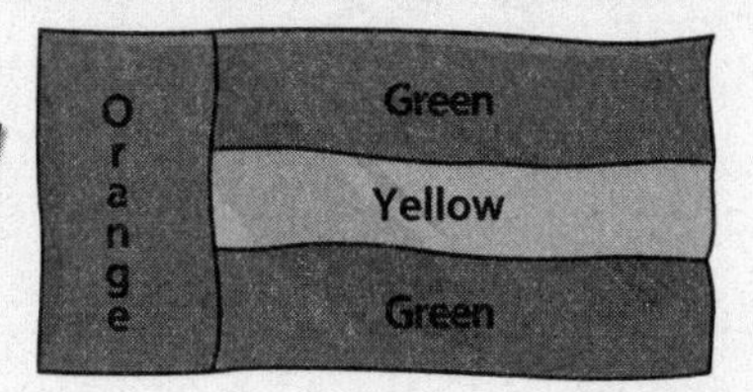

What do you **KNOW** from the information stated in the problem?	
What do you **KNOW** from the information shown in the image?	
What information do you **NOT** need to know to solve the problem?	
WHAT exactly does the problem want you to find?	
What **STRATEGY** or operation will you use to solve this problem?	

Name ________________________

Enrichment
6-6

Time for Lunch?

A school day is 6 hours and 39 minutes. The school has 7 periods for classes. Solve the problems. Write the hidden questions. Write equations to show each step. Be sure to define your variables.

1. If you divide the school day into 7 equal periods, how many minutes, *p*, would be in each period? There are 60 minutes in 1 hour.

Hidden question: ________________________

____

Equations: ________________________

____

Solution: ________________________

2. How many minutes would be in each period, *p*, if you subtract 40 minutes for lunch and 16 minutes for homeroom?

Hidden question: ________________________

____

Equations: ________________________

____

Solution: ________________________

3. Complete the schedule using the times you found.

Activity	Start Time	Activity	Start Time
Homeroom	8:15	Lunch	11:47
Math		Reading	
Writing		Social Studies	
Art or Music		Gym	
Science		School's Out	

Name ______________________________

Factors and Multiples

Dear Family,

Your child is learning about factors. In this topic, he or she will use arrays and multiplication to find the factors of a given number. The concept is extended to include factor pairs, lists of factors, and prime and composite numbers. Your child will also learn that factors are related to multiples which will prepare him or her for working with fractions.

12 objects can be arranged into six different rectangular arrays.

Arrays	Expressions	Factor Pairs	Factors of 12
	1 × 12	1 and 12	1, 2, 3, 4, 6, 12
	12 × 1		
	2 × 6	2 and 6	
	6 × 2		
	3 × 4	3 and 4	
	4 × 3		

How Many Ways?

Materials uniform objects such as pennies, paper and pencil

Say a number. Have your child show all the ways to arrange that number of objects in rectangular arrays. Record each arrangement as a multiplication expression. Talk about why some arrangements do not work.

Observe Your Child

After recording all the possible expressions in the activity above, have your child look for patterns in the factors of the expressions and use that pattern to identify the factor pairs.

Nombre ______________________________

De la escuela al hogar (en español)
Tema 7

Factores y múltiplos

Estimada familia:

Su niño(a) está aprendiendo sobre factores. En este tema, usará matrices y la multiplicación para hallar los factores de un número dado. El concepto se amplía para incluir pares de factores, listas de factores y números primos y compuestos. Su niño(a) también aprenderá que los factores se relacionan con los múltiplos, y eso le servirá para trabajar con fracciones.

Se pueden acomodar 12 objetos en seis matrices rectangulares distintas.

Matrices	Expresiones	Pares de factores	Factores de 12
	1 × 12	1 y 12	1, 2, 3, 4, 6, 12
	12 × 1		
	2 × 6	2 y 6	
	6 × 2		
	3 × 4	3 y 4	
	4 × 3		

¿De cuántas maneras?

Materiales objetos uniformes, como monedas de 1¢, papel y lápiz

Diga un número. Pida a su niño(a) que muestre todas las maneras de ordenar esa cantidad de objetos en matrices rectangulares. Anoten cada ordenación como una expresión de multiplicación. Comenten por qué algunas ordenaciones no funcionan.

Observe a su niño(a)

Después de anotar todas las expresiones posibles en la actividad anterior, pida a su niño(a) que busque patrones en los factores de las expresiones y que los use para identificar los pares de factores.

Name ______________________________

Pick a Project

Project 7A

Mammoth Cave National Park

Mammoth Cave National Park is in Kentucky, and it is known to have one of the longest cave systems in North America.

Once you arrive at the park, there is plenty to do. You can take cave tours, hike, swim, and fish among other things.

While visiting or vacationing at Mammoth Cave National Park, people can stay at a nearby hotel or stay at one of the campgrounds. Some people stay in campers while others stay at camp sights and sleep in tents.

Your Project Model a Campground

Some campers must bring everything they need to some campgrounds. Other campgrounds provide some supplies, such as campfire pits, cooking grills, bathrooms, showers, and even electricity. Design a campground in which each campsite can hold at most 6 campers. Make a model of your campground. Try to come up with an interesting and unusual design.

Decide how you want to show people in each campsite. First, use your model to show the campground as completely full. Then, use your model to represent addition and subtraction problems. Describe a situation to go along with each problem. For example, "There were 30 people at the campground, and then 6 people left ($30 - 6 = 24$)." Or "There were 12 people at the campground, and then 8 more people came ($12 + 8 = 20$)."

Write your own problems, and model them.

Name ____________________

Pick a Project

Project 7B

College Basketball Arenas

Many universities and colleges have basketball teams for both women and men. The first women's and the first men's intercollegiate basketball games were both held in 1896.

Basketball is played on a court inside of a building that is called an arena. Some universities have arenas that can hold a lot of people. The Carrier Dome at Syracuse University in New York has seats for over 33,000 fans!

Your Project Create a Basketball Poster

Do research to find the name of 4 colleges or universities that have women's or men's basketball teams.

Make a poster. List the following:

- The name of the college or university
- The name of the arena where the team plays
- The number of fans that each arena can hold
- Tell if that number is prime or composite.
- Round the number of fans that each arena can hold to the nearest thousand.

List the arenas in order from the arena that can hold the fewest number of fans to the arena that can hold the greatest number of fans. Find the difference between the number of seats in the largest and smallest arenas.

Name ____________________

Pick a Project

Project 7C

Arranging Arrays

Stores that sell plants will display them in different ways.

Sometimes potted plants are organized in arrangements so that there are the same number of potted plants in each row and column. These plants are arranged in arrays.

Plants can be displayed in just 1 long row of potted plants or in several rows of potted plants with the same number of plants in each row and column. The different arrays make the potted plants look interesting and are easy for customers to see.

Your Project Design a Plant Array for a Store Display

You own a plant store and will design several displays of potted plants.

You have the following:

24 pots with tomatoes
56 pots with ferns
72 pots with daisies
45 pots with cactuses

Show two ways that you could display each type of plant. Use arrays for your displays. None of your arrays should have just 1 long row. Label the type of plant that you will display in each array.

Finally, present your plan for your displays to your class. Explain how the number of rows and columns show the total number of pots in each display.

Name ___________________________

enVision® STEM Activity 7-1

Feeding the Animals

Did You Know? Animals have specific nutritional requirements. Zookeepers determine how much protein, fat, fiber, carbohydrates, and vitamins each animal needs. Zookeepers have to keep track of what types of foods and how much food animals eat each day.

Animal	Number of Animals
Elephant	6
Dolphin	8
Giraffe	10
Penguin	30
Snake	15

The table above shows the number of each type of animal the zookeeper feeds each day. Suppose animals could be arranged in the feeding areas in different ways.

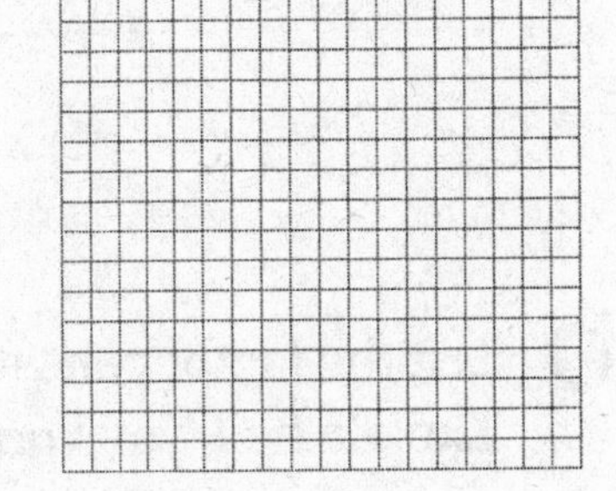

1. Use the grid to show all the possible ways the zookeeper could arrange the elephants during feeding time.

2. What are the factors of 6?

____

3. How many different arrays could the zookeeper make to arrange the penguins into feeding areas during feeding time?

____

4. What are the factors of 30?

____

5. **Extension** The zookeeper would be able to arrange all but one of the animals into feeding-area arrays with two rows. For which animal would an array with two rows **NOT** be possible? Explain.

____

____

Name ______________________

enVision® STEM Activity 7-3

Schools of Fish

Did You Know? A group of fish is called a school. Fish travel in schools as a form of protection from predators. The idea of "safety in numbers" is especially beneficial for young and small fish. Small fish form dense schools and move in unison. This discourages predators.

1. One school of fish contains a total of 12 fish. How many different arrays can be formed with 12 fish? Draw each array.

2. List the factor pairs for a school of fish containing 48 fish. Explain how you know you have listed all of the factor pairs.

3. **Extension** Scientists believe that a school of fish that can form an array with an equal (or close to equal) number of fish in the rows and columns will have a greater chance of survival. List all possible arrays for a school of fish containing 81 fish. List all possible arrays for a school of fish containing 92 fish. Which array provides the best chance of survival? Explain.

Name ______________________

Daily Review

7-1

1. Alex scored 20 points in the basketball game, which is 4 times as many points as Tony scored. How many points did Tony score?

Ⓐ 5 points
Ⓑ 16 points
Ⓒ 24 points
Ⓓ 80 points

2. Which number rounds to 140,000 when rounded to the nearest ten thousand?

Ⓐ 124,641
Ⓑ 134,798
Ⓒ 138,982
Ⓓ 149,641

3. There are 35 chairs and 8 tables in the art room. The art teacher wants to put an equal number of chairs at each table. How many chairs will be at each table? How many chairs will be left over?

Ⓐ 4 chairs at each table; 1 chair left over

Ⓑ 4 chairs at each table; 3 chairs left over

Ⓒ 5 chairs at each table; 3 chairs left over

Ⓓ 5 chairs at each table; 5 chairs left over

4. Which is the number name for 32,492?

Ⓐ thirty thousand, four hundred ninety-two

Ⓑ thirty-two thousand, four hundred two

Ⓒ thirty-two hundred, four hundred ninety-two

Ⓓ thirty-two thousand, four hundred ninety-two

5. Candace makes $8 per hour at her job. Last month she worked 38 hours. She also made $65 babysitting last month. How much money did Candace earn last month? Show your work.

____

____

6. Draw an area model and use partial products to find 15×18.

____

7. Tyrone drove 372 miles in 6 hours. Use compatible numbers to estimate how many miles Tyrone drove each hour.

____

8. An elementary school spent $143,250 on repairs to the building. The middle school spent $235,500 on repairs. How much did the two schools spend for repairs?

____

Name ______________________________

Reteach to Build Understanding
7-1

Vocabulary

1. Numbers multiplied together to find a product are called **factors**.

$4 \times 6 = 24$
Factors

$2 \times 3 \times 7 = 42$
Factors

The factors are ______ and ______.

The product is ______.

The factors are ______, ______, and ______.

The product is ______.

2. What are the factors of 8?

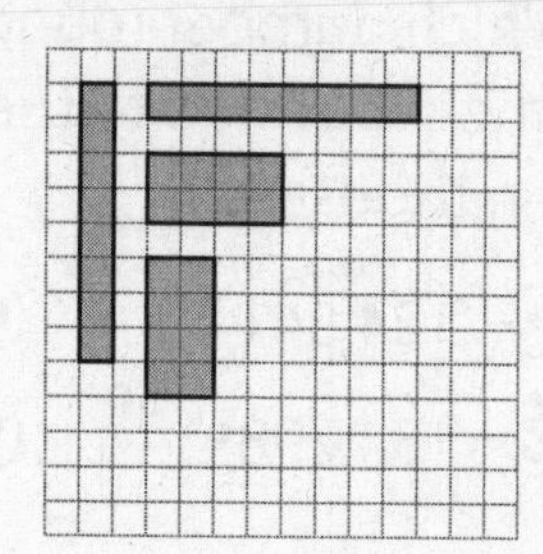

Use the arrays to help write the missing factors.

1 row of 8 ______ $\times 8 = 8$

8 rows of 1 ______ $\times 1 = 8$

2 rows of 4 ______ $\times 4 = 8$

4 rows of 2 ______ $\times 2 = 8$

There are ______ possible ways to arrange 8.

List the factors of 8.

______, ______, ______, ______

3. Draw all the possible arrays for 16 on the grid at the right.

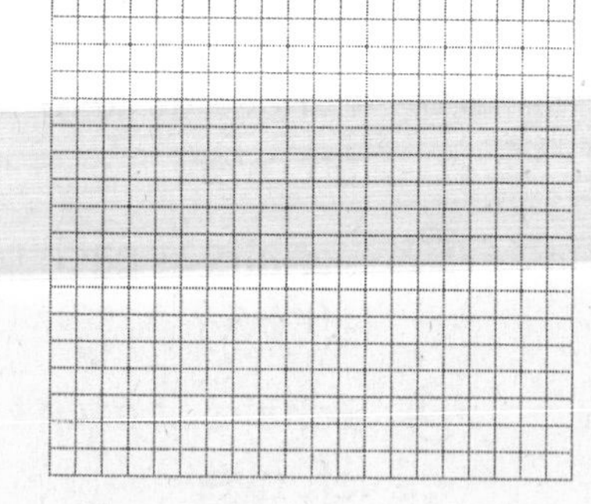

There are ______ possible arrays for 16.

Use the arrays to help write the factors.

______ row of 16 ______ $\times$ ______ $= 16$

______ rows of 1 ______ $\times$ ______ $= 16$

______ rows of 8 ______ $\times$ ______ $= 16$

______ rows of 2 ______ $\times$ ______ $= 16$

______ rows of 4 ______ $\times$ ______ $= 16$

List the factors of 16.

______, ______, ______, ______, ______

On the Back!

4. Find all the possible factors of 18. Use a grid to help.

Name ______________________________

Build Mathematical Literacy
7-1

Read the problem. Answer the questions to help understand the problem.

Jane says 5 is a factor of every whole number that has a 5 in the ones place. Fred says 5 is a factor of every whole number that has a 0 in the ones place. Who is correct? Explain.

Examine Jane's Claim

1. What is Jane's claim?

____

____

2. Give an example that illustrates Jane's claim. If it's not possible, explain why.

____

3. Give an example that disproves Jane's claim. If it's not possible, explain why.

____

____

____

Examine Fred's Claim

4. What is Fred's claim?

____

____

5. Give an example that illustrates Fred's claim. If it's not possible, explain why.

____

6. Give an example that disproves Fred's claim. If it's not possible, explain why.

____

____

____

Name ______________________________

Enrichment
7-1

Factor Conjectures

A conjecture is a statement that is believed to be true but which has not been proven. Complete each table. Use the table to complete the conjecture.

1. Conjecture: If 3 is a factor of a number, 3 is also a factor of

______________________________.

Number	39	62	72	87	89	93
Is 3 a factor of number?	Yes					
Sum of digits	12					
Is 3 a factor of sum?	Yes					

2. Conjecture: If a number is even, it has a factor of 2. If a number is odd,

______________________________.

Number	44	57	65	76	83	99
Even or odd?	Even					
Is 2 a factor of number?	Yes					

3. Conjecture: If 2 and 3 are factors of a number,

______________________________.

Number	42	53	64	75	84	96
Is 2 a factor of number?						
Is 3 a factor of number?						
Is 6 a factor of number?						

Name ______________________________

Daily Review

7-2

1. Juan has 216 beach balls. Each beach ball has 6 stripes. How many stripes are there in all?

Ⓐ 1,266 stripes

Ⓑ 1,272 stripes

Ⓒ 1,296 stripes

Ⓓ 1,386 stripes

2. An apple orchard has 224 golden-apple trees. There are 8 equal rows of golden-apple trees. How many golden-apple trees are in each row?

Ⓐ 28 trees

Ⓑ 72 trees

Ⓒ 216 trees

Ⓓ 236 trees

3. Four friends equally share a collection of 2,232 stickers. How many stickers will each friend receive?

Ⓐ 747 stickers

Ⓑ 601 stickers

Ⓒ 581 stickers

Ⓓ 558 stickers

4. Which equation represents the statement, 42 is 6 times as many as 7?

Ⓐ $42 = 6 \times 7$

Ⓑ $13 = 6 + 7$

Ⓒ $42 \times 6 = 252$

Ⓓ $42 \times 7 = 294$

5. How many marbles are left if 9 friends equally share a package of 75 marbles?

____

6. Roberto has 2 books with 319 pages each, and 3 books with 264 pages each. How many pages are there all together?

____

7. There are 30 chairs in the band room. Mr. Avery wants to have the same number of chairs in each row. There must be more than 1 row, and the number of chairs in each row must also be greater than the number of rows. Explain how Mr. Avery could arrange the chairs.

____

____

____

____

8. Is the number of factor pairs for a number equal to the number of arrays for the same number? Explain.

____

____

____

Name ______________________

Reteach to Build Understanding
7-2

Vocabulary

1. **Factor pairs** are two numbers that when multiplied give a certain product.

The factors of 6 are 1, 2, 3, and 6. Find which pairs of factors have a product of 6.

$1 \times 2 =$ ______ Are 1 and 2 a factor pair for 6? ______

$2 \times 3 =$ ______ Are 2 and 3 a factor pair for 6? ______

2. Find the factor pairs for 14.

First, find the factors of 14.

____

1 group of 14

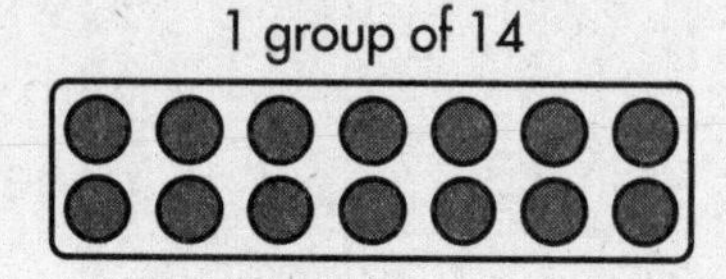

14 groups of 1

7 groups of 2

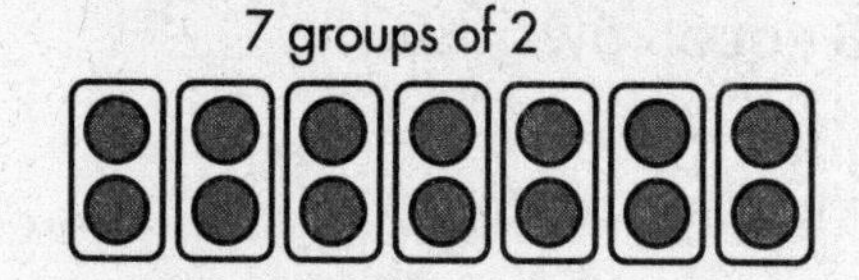

2 groups of 7

Determine which pairs of factors have a product of 14.

$1 \times$ ______ $= 14$ and ______ $\times 1 = 14$

$2 \times$ ______ $= 14$ and ______ $\times 2 = 14$

The factor pairs for 14 are:

1 and ______

2 and ______

3. Find the factor pairs for 24.

1 group of ______ or 24 groups of ______ 3 groups of ______ or 8 groups of ______

2 groups of ______ or 12 groups of ______ 4 groups of ______ or 6 groups of ______

The factor pairs are ______________________________________.

Write the factor pairs.

4. 37

5. 94

6. 65

On the Back!

7. Write the factor pairs for 40.

Name ______________________

Build Mathematical Literacy
7-2

Read the problem. Answer the questions to help understand the problem.

Higher Order Thinking If a blue whale is 9 times as long as the manatee shown, how much longer is the blue whale than the manatee? Write and solve equations.

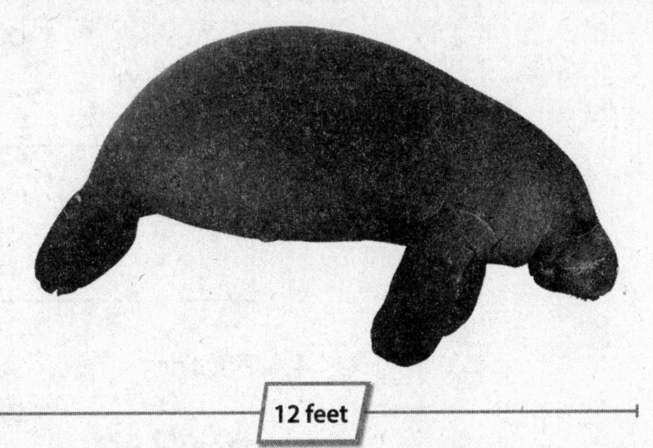

12 feet

1. How long is the manatee shown?

Ⓐ 9 feet long
Ⓑ 12 feet long
Ⓒ 108 feet long
Ⓓ The information isn't given in the problem.

2. Which operation should you use to represent the statement "9 times as long"?

Ⓐ Addition
Ⓑ Subtraction
Ⓒ Multiplication
Ⓓ Division

3. If b represents the length of the blue whale, which equation represents the relationship between the length of the blue whale and the length of the manatee?

Ⓐ $9 + 12 = b$
Ⓑ $12 - 9 = b$
Ⓒ $9 \times 12 = b$
Ⓓ $12 \div 9 = b$

4. Which of the following has the same meaning as "How much longer is the blue whale than the manatee?"

Ⓐ What is the total length of the blue whale and the manatee?
Ⓑ What is the difference in length between the manatee and the blue whale?
Ⓒ How long is the manatee?
Ⓓ How much longer is the manatee than the blue whale?

Name ______________________

Multiples or Factors?

Look at the numbers in each box.
Circle if they are multiples or factors, and write the number.

1. Factors
of ________
Multiples

6 2
3 1

2. Factors
of ________
Multiples

16 40
24 56

3. Factors
of ________
Multiples

15 25
40

4. Factors
of ________
Multiples

2
4
1

Read the label for each box.
Write at least three numbers in each box that match the description.

5. Multiples of 3

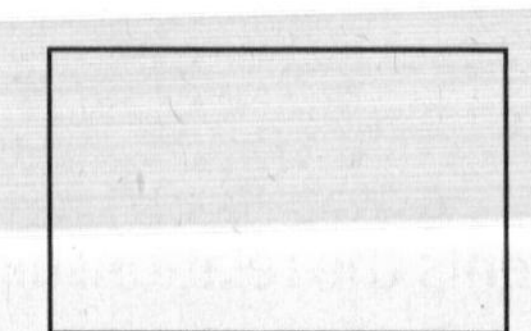

6. Factors of 9

7. Factors of 8

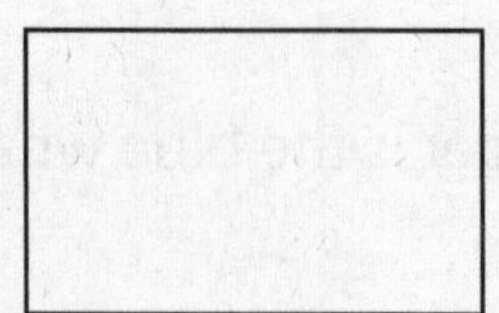

8. Multiples of 7

Name ______________________

Daily Review
7-3

1. Camden has 74 quarters. He puts the quarters in stacks of 4. How many stacks of 4 quarters did Camden make?

Ⓐ 1 stack
Ⓑ 18 stacks
Ⓒ 19 stacks
Ⓓ 20 stacks

2. A pizza shop sold 18 medium pizzas. The number of large pizzas sold was 3 times as many as the number of medium pizzas sold. How many pizzas did the pizza shop sell altogether?

Ⓐ 36 pizzas
Ⓑ 39 pizzas
Ⓒ 54 pizzas
Ⓓ 72 pizzas

3. A garden is 34 feet wide and 52 feet long. What is the area of the garden?

Ⓐ 172 square feet
Ⓑ 1,500 square feet
Ⓒ 1,568 square feet
Ⓓ 1,768 square feet

4. Which of the following are factors of both 24 and 36? Select all that apply.

☐ 3
☐ 4
☐ 6
☐ 8
☐ 12

5. Oak Grove has a population of 38,700 people. Write 38,700 in expanded form.

____

6. The Holt family is purchasing 4 cell phones. Store A sells 3 cell phones that cost $165 each, which includes a fourth phone for free. Store B sells the same cell phone for $135 each. Which store has the better deal for purchasing 4 cell phones? Explain.

____

____

____

____

7. The school auditorium has 120 seats. The school is selling tickets for 3 performances of the school play. How many tickets are still available? Show your work.

Day	Number of Tickets Sold
Friday	102
Saturday	96
Sunday	118

____

____

____

____

Name ______________________

Reteach to Build Understanding
7-3

Vocabulary

1. When factor pairs start repeating, you can make a general statement, or **generalize**, that all of the factors of a number are listed.

To find all the factors for 20, begin dividing by 1. When the quotient has no remainder, you have found a factor. Use the division fact to write a related multiplication problem, and then use the Commutative Property to write another multiplication equation.

1 2 4 5 10 20

$20 \div 1 = 20$	$1 \times 20 = 20$ and $20 \times 1 = 20$	
$20 \div 2 = 10$	$2 \times 10 = 20$ and $10 \times 2 = 20$	
$20 \div 3 = 6$ R2	3 is not a factor.	
$20 \div 4 = 5$	$4 \times 5 = 20$ and $5 \times 4 = 20$	

Since you found the factor paired with 5, stop checking for factors. The factor pairs start repeating. You can generalize that all the factors for 20 have been found.

The factor pairs for 20 are

_____ and _____, _____ and _____, _____ and _____.

2. Find the factors for 32.

$32 \div 1 =$ _____ $1 \times 32 = 32$ and _____ $\times 1 = 32$

$32 \div 2 =$ _____ $2 \times$ _____ $= 32$ and $16 \times 2 = 32$

$32 \div 3 =$ _____ 3 is not a factor.

$32 \div 4 =$ _____ $4 \times$ _____ $= 32$ and $8 \times$ _____ $= 32$

5, 6, and 7 are not factors.

$32 \div 8 =$ _____ $8 \times$ _____ $= 32$ and $4 \times$ _____ $= 32$

What is the first factor pair that repeats? _______

The factor pairs for 32 are _____ and _____, _____ and _____,

_____ and _____.

On the Back!

3. Find all the factors for 72.

Name ____________________

Read the problem. Answer the questions to help understand how to solve the problem.

A pet store needs 3 displays with the products shown. The boxes of kitty litter need to be stacked with the same number of boxes in each row. There needs to be at least 3 rows with at least 3 boxes in each row. What are all the ways the boxes of kitty litter could be stacked?

50 fish bowls

48 boxes of kitty litter

88 bags of dog food

What are all the ways the boxes of kitty litter can be stacked in at least 3 rows with at least 3 boxes in each row?

What do you **KNOW** from the information stated in the problem?	
What do you **KNOW** from the information shown in the image?	
What information do you **NOT** need to know to solve the problem?	
WHAT exactly does the problem want you to find?	
What **STRATEGY** or operation will you use to solve this problem?	

Name ______________________________

Where Does the Repeating Start?

When you list all the factors of a number in order, the factors pair up as shown in the diagram. The factors are symmetric on either side of a "mirror" line as shown by the dashed line in the diagram.

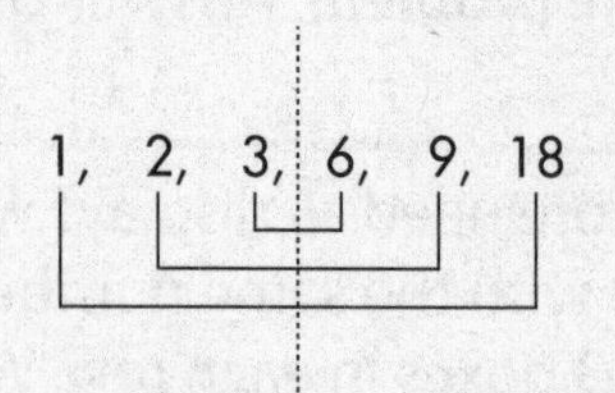

Answer the following questions to discover how to find this mirror line for any number to help you list all the factors.

1. You can find the square of a number by multiplying the number by itself. For example, the square of 2 is $2 \times 2 = 4$. Complete the table by finding the square of each number.

Number	1	2	3	4	5	6	7	8	9	10
Square	1	4								

2. The factors of 18 are shown in the diagram at the top. The number 18 is between which two square numbers?

18 is between ______ and ______

Notice, 16 is the square of 4, and 25 is the square of 5. The mirror line is between 4 and 5.

3. Complete the table. Is the mirror line where it is expected each time?

Number	**Square Numbers Number is Between**	**Mirror Line Should Be Between**	**Factors**	**Where Expected?**
33	25 and 36	5 and 6		
45				
50				
85				

Name ___________________________

Daily Review

7-4

1. Kevin is putting his baseball cards into an album. He has 450 cards and each page of the album holds 9 cards. How many pages will Kevin need if all 450 baseball cards are going in the album?

Ⓐ 50 pages
Ⓑ 40 pages
Ⓒ 25 pages
Ⓓ 5 pages

2. The population of Town A is 15,729. Town B has a population of 21,634. What is the total population of the two towns?

Ⓐ 35,372 people
Ⓑ 36,799 people
Ⓒ 37,255 people
Ⓓ 37,363 people

3. Wendy has 8 kinds of seashells in her collection. She has 122 of each kind of shell. How many seashells does Wendy have in her collection?

Ⓐ 976 seashells
Ⓑ 866 seashells
Ⓒ 130 seashells
Ⓓ 114 seashells

4. Select all of the factors of 18.

☐ 1
☐ 2
☐ 3
☐ 6
☐ 9

5. The population of Andrew's city is 172,648. About how many people live in Andrew's city rounded to the nearest thousand?

____

6. Write all the ways you can express 24 as the product of 2 whole numbers.

____

____

____

____

7. Jaine has saved 7 times as much money as Jared has saved. Jaine has saved $378. How much money has Jared saved?

____

8. Use the grid to show all the possible rectangular arrays for 8.

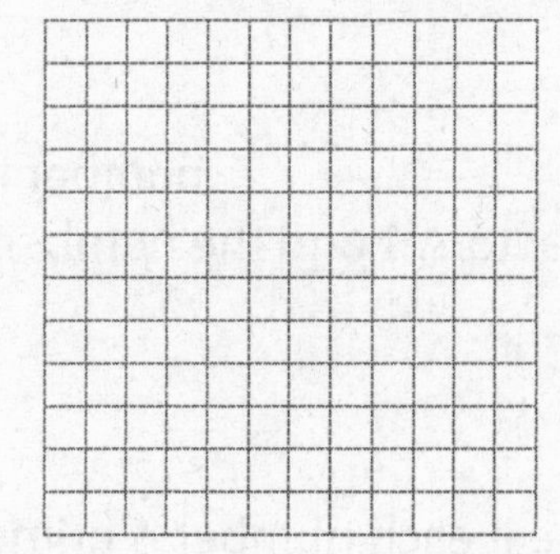

Name ______________________________

Vocabulary

1. A **prime number** is a whole number greater than 1 that has exactly 2 factors, 1 and itself.

   Circle the prime numbers:

2	**3**	**4**	**5**	**6**	**7**	**8**
1×2	1×3	1×4	1×5	1×6	1×7	1×8
		2×2		2×3		2×4

2. A **composite number** is a whole number greater than 1 that has more than 2 factors.

   Circle the composite numbers.

2	**3**	**4**	**5**	**6**	**7**	**8**
1×2	1×3	1×4	1×5	1×6	1×7	1×8
		2×2		2×3		2×4

3. Is 18 a prime or a composite number?
   Use the arrays at the right to name the factors of 18.

   Factors of 18:

   ______, ______, ______, ______, ______, ______

   18 is a ______________ number because it has more than two factors.

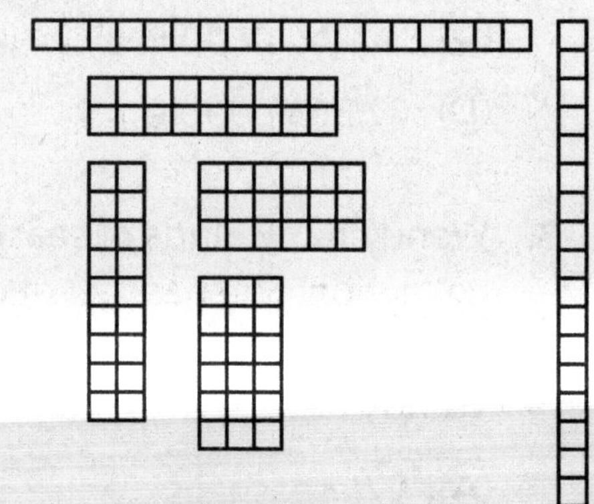

4. Is 11 a prime or composite number?
   Use the arrays at the right to name the factors of 11.

   Factors of 11:

   ______, ______

   11 is a ______________ number because it only has two factors, 1 and the number itself.

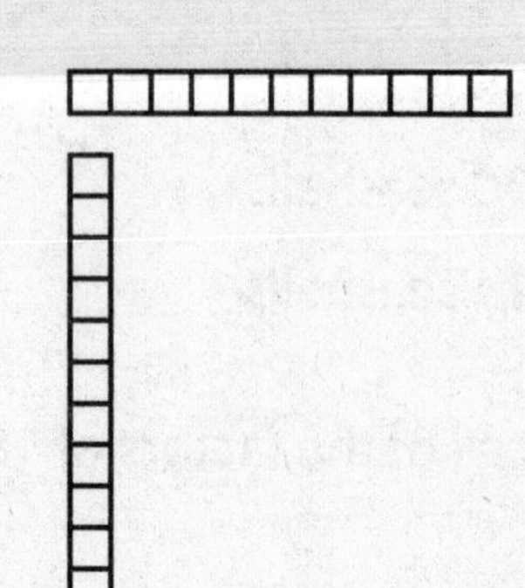

On the Back!

5. Determine if each number is prime or composite.
   Draw arrays for each.

   15 19

Name ______________________

Read the problem. Answer the questions to help understand the problem.

Critique Reasoning Greta says the product of two prime numbers must also be prime. Joan disagreed. Who is correct?

Survey

1. What is the problem about?

Question

2. What question will be answered by solving the problem?

Reread

3. Underline Greta's claim.

Question

4. What is Joan's claim?

Construct

5. Create an example that supports either Greta's claim or Joan's claim. Whose claim does it support?

Question

6. How can you use the definition of a prime number to explain your answer to Exercise 5?

Name ______________________

Enrichment
7-4

Prime Time

Remember that a prime number is a whole number greater than 1 that has exactly two factors, itself and 1.

Every number greater than 5 can be written as the sum of three prime numbers. For example, 13 can be written as the sum of $3 + 3 + 7$.

Express the numbers below as the sum of three prime numbers. Write the primes in the squares.

1. ☐ + ☐ + ☐ = 17

2. ☐ + ☐ + ☐ = 10

3. ☐ + ☐ + ☐ = 15

4. ☐ + ☐ + ☐ = 21

5. ☐ + ☐ + ☐ = 32

6. ☐ + ☐ + ☐ = 30

7. ☐ + ☐ + ☐ = 26

8. ☐ + ☐ + ☐ = 50

Name ______________________

Daily Review
7-5

1. Which number has an odd number of factors?

Ⓐ 56
Ⓑ 25
Ⓒ 18
Ⓓ 15

2. Shawn has a set of 125 marbles. He is organizing his marbles into 5 equal groups. How many marbles should he put in each group?

Ⓐ 10 marbles
Ⓑ 15 marbles
Ⓒ 20 marbles
Ⓓ 25 marbles

3. Rachel has 3 times as many roses as carnations. She has 12 fewer carnations than daisies. There are 15 daisies. How many flowers does Rachel have in all?

Ⓐ 63 flowers
Ⓑ 42 flowers
Ⓒ 27 flowers
Ⓓ 21 flowers

4. Which is the expanded form of 450,082?

Ⓐ 450 + 82
Ⓑ 40,000 + 5,000 + 80 + 2
Ⓒ 400,000 + 500 + 80 + 2
Ⓓ 400,000 + 50,000 + 80 + 2

5. Maria says 1, 2, 3, 4, 6, and 12 are all the factors of a number. What is the number?

____

6. Jim has 1,337 crickets. He sells the crickets in groups of 6. How many groups of 6 crickets can Jim sell? How many crickets will be in the remaining group?

____

____

____

7. Rita says all numbers have an even number of factors. She gives two examples. The number 3 has two factors: 1 and 3. The number 6 has four factors: 1, 2, 3, and 6. Write a number that has an odd number of factors. Then list the factors.

____

____

8. Find the sum and difference of 147,167 and 204,107.

____

Name ______________________________

Reteach to Build Understanding
7-5

Vocabulary

1. A **multiple** is the product of a given factor and a whole number. You can use a multiplication chart to help find some multiples for numbers.

List some multiples of 5.

Step 1: Find the column (or row) for 5.

Step 2: All the numbers in that column (or row) are multiples of 5.

Multiples of 5, in the chart, are:

5, 10, ____, ____, ____, 30, 35, ____, ____

×	1	2	3	4	5	6	7	8	9
1	1	2	3	4	5	6	7	8	9
2	2	4	6	8	10	12	14	16	18
3	3	6	9	12	15	18	21	24	27
4	4	8	12	16	20	24	28	32	36
5	5	10	15	20	25	30	35	40	45
6	6	12	18	24	30	36	42	48	54
7	7	14	21	28	35	42	49	56	63
8	8	16	24	32	40	48	56	64	72
9	9	18	27	36	45	54	63	72	81

2. What are some multiples of 8? Use the multiplication chart above.

Step 1: Find the column (or row) for 8.

Step 2: All the numbers in that column (or row) are multiples of 8.

In the chart, the multiples of 8 are:

8, 16, ____, ____, ____, ____, ____, ____, 72

3. Is 48 a multiple of 6?

Think: What number times 6 equals 48? ____

48 is a multiple of 6 because 6 times ____ equals 48.

4. Is 39 a multiple of 9?

Think: What number times 9 equals 39?

39 is not a multiple of 9 because ______________________________

______________________________.

On the Back!

5. Write 5 multiples of each number.

6 12 15

Name ______________________________

Read the problem. Reread each of the statements from the problem. Then, complete the steps to help understand the problem.

Isabel wrote this mystery problem: The quotient is a multiple of 6. The dividend is a multiple of 9. The divisor is a factor of 12. Find one possible solution to Isabel's mystery problem.

The quotient is a multiple of 6.

1. Write a division equation. Circle the quotient.

____

2. Write a number that is a multiple of 6.

____

The dividend is a multiple of 9.

3. Underline the dividend in your equation from Exercise 1.

4. Write a number that is a multiple of 9.

____

The divisor is a factor of 12.

5. Draw a square around the divisor in your equation from Exercise 1.

6. Write a number that is a factor of 12.

____

Thinking

7. Is there only one solution to Isabel's mystery problem? Explain.

____

____

Name ____________________

Enrichment
7-5

Multiple Statements

Tell whether or not each of the statements about multiples is true. Give at least two examples to support that it is true or one counterexample to show that it is NOT true.

1. All multiples of 5 have 0 or 5 in ones place.

2. If a number is a multiple of 3, it is a multiple of 12.

3. All whole numbers are a multiple of 1.

4. If a number is even, it is a multiple of 4.

5. If a number m is a multiple of another number n, then n is a factor of m.